G000241542

Lawyers' Tales

Lawyers' Tales

JOHN GRAY

Foreword by
SIR GEOFFREY VOS

Canis Press

Published by Canis Press
Ashford
Kent
TN25 7AZ

First published in Great Britain 2010
Copyright © John Gray 2010

ISBN 978-0-9548878-9-6

A catalogue record of this book is available from the British Library

Design, typesetting and production by
John Saunders Design & Production, Abingdon OX13 5HU
Printed in Great Britain by
The MPG Books Group, Bodmin and King's Lynn

FOREWORD

John Gray, the author of this splendid volume, was my first and finest pupil master. I learnt so much from him about the law, about life, and, most of all, about the people who populate the legal profession. He was and is a meticulous observer. In the 6 happy months I spent with him, I learnt that John Gray has a knack for telling a story, which I see now exemplified in these tales, some of which have their origins in my time as a pupil with him.

John Gray is a perfectionist, who taught me that the most terrifying thing about the Bar is the possibility of getting the advice wrong. It always seemed to me that there was no chance of his doing that, since he always worked so hard to ensure that every aspect of the case was checked and researched before he finalised his opinions. He entertained self-doubt in a way that is, at once, charming and agonising. In these tales, he has demonstrated this approach, and done what he has always done with such precision, namely provided his extraordinarily insightful observations of legal life.

There are many books that poke fun, harmless or otherwise, at the more pompous and self-satisfied judges and members of the legal profession, but that is not the objective of *Lawyers' Tales*. Instead, each of these stories provides a thoughtful and humourous insight into the trials and tribulations of the late 20th century legal practitioner.

John Gray is to be congratulated on assembling a marvellous collection of anecdotes and sharply focused tales of legal life centred on the Inns of Court. His uniquely good-natured wit shines through. The collection shows how he is able to see the ironies in every situation, and to identify the lesson to be learnt and the moral to be drawn.

I whole-heartedly recommend *Lawyers' Tales* to anyone who wants to know a little more about the hopes, fears and aspirations of the legal practitioner. Every appearance in a civil or criminal court provides another opportunity for anxiety, error and, most of all, humour. John Gray has provided us all with a unique collection of such incidents. It will be enjoyed by all those with any interest in the English Legal System, and can be read as a piece or dipped into with equal pleasure.

Sir Geoffrey Vos
London, July 2010

CONTENTS

ILLUSTRATIONS

For a note on the illustrations see p. x

AUTHOR'S NOTE ON ILLUSTRATIONS

Illustrations are by Norman Mansbridge, Peter Brookes, Susan Gray and William (Bill) Papas. With the exception of those drawn by Susan Gray, none was produced specifically for this book. Those of Norman Mansbridge are from the 1960s, drawn for the Daily Sketch and Punch. He was a friend of my parents and drew pictures for me as a small boy. With the much appreciated help of Mr Chris Beetles (whose Gallery is at 8 and 10 Ryder Street London SW1Y 6QB), I traced his daughter, Ann, with whose kind permission and assistance five pieces of his work are reproduced.

His original captions are now of course outdated and their relevance to my text is not always obvious. For reasons of sentiment however I was anxious to include these works, so I have done so and added captions related to the content of the numbered tale to which it relates.

Peter Brookes is the leading cartoonist for The Times. His portrayal of barristers following collapse of the Leed's trial has amused me since I cut it out of my newspaper in April 2001. It is for me, as a sometime lawyer, a delightful example of the cartoonist's barbed ridicule. With a further caption it is on page xvii.

Susan Gray (Susie) is my wife. An accomplished artist and calligrapher she was unwilling notwithstanding to attempt cartoons. She was kind enough however to draw *inter alia* the fungi ('shaggy cap . . . lawyer's wig', on front of the jacket and at pages xv and 23) and all our animals to whom this book is dedicated.

William (Bill) Papas was cartoonist for the Guardian. In the 1960s he illustrated a book for the Oxford University Press entitled 'The Law.' Three of his drawings from that volume are reproduced by kind permission of Tessa Papas. His sketch of the Royal Courts of Justice, related to several tales, portrays the very hub of the law in England and Wales and appears isolated on pages 82 and 83.

TO

*My special big lurcher dog, the late Bertie departed this life on
2nd December 2009. RIP
My little lurcher dog Ivo. My puppy lurcher, son of Ivo,
Raffa (Rafael). My wife's pony Apollo, Her Shetland pony Poppy
Our two half-Siamese cats, Charlie and Dido.
My wife's pet sheep: Cleopatra, Larry, Florian and Aida.
Bertie (Cuthbert) foxhound/greyhound cross had become the logo of
Canis Press. All identified above are to be seen below, drawn by
my wife Susie.*

ACKNOWLEDGEMENTS

My thanks to:

Ann Mansbridge for permission to reproduce Norman Mansbridge's drawing of overcrowding in the London Underground (date unknown) and four other of his cartoons identified at page ix © The Estate of Norman Mansbridge.

NI Syndication and to Mr Peter Brookes, Political Cartoonist for permission to reproduce a cartoon drawn by Mr Brookes and published in The Times on 11th April 2001 and 9th May 2009. © The Times /nisyndication.com

Tessa Papas for permission to reproduce three sketches from 'The Law' published by Oxford University Press 1960, more particularly identified, as of Bow Street, of The Royal Courts of Justice, and of three Judges of the Court of Appeal in England. © Estate of William Papas.

EXPLANATION OF SOME EXPRESSIONS

Assizes. Sittings of High Court judges in specified towns while travelling in circuits around the country with commissions from the Crown to try cases. Commissions were of oyer and terminer and general gaol delivery. Those accused of serious criminal offences (felonies) were held until the arrival of the judge, when they were delivered from gaol, tried and in earlier times, if found guilty, too often hanged.

A commission of *nisi prius* (unless sooner or before') empowered the 'assize judge' to try civil cases. Explanation of *nisi prius* is too lengthy for here. Look to John Gray's Lawyers' Latin new edition at page 94. Assizes were abolished by the Courts Act 1971. Their criminal jurisdiction has been transferred to the Crown Court and the High Court is empowered to hear civil cases anywhere in England or Wales without the need for a commission.

Barrister Junior and Senior. After passing all qualifying examinations and fulfilling all other requirements and being called to the Bar by whichever of the four Inns of Court he or she had joined (Lincoln's Inn, Inner Temple, Middle Temple and Gray's Inn) an aspiring lawyer will become a Junior Barrister. He or she will so remain unless and until he or she takes silk and becomes Queen's (or as appropriate, King's) Counsel, QC or KC.

At an indeterminate age (between 30 and 35 or after ten years from call, when pupils may be taken) a Barrister will, as a matter of practice or convention, usually to mark age and experience, come to be described as a Senior Junior. Some never take silk either because they prefer the mainly written and pleading work of the junior and do not ask to be considered for the more courtroom orientated and generally only heavier leading work, or are refused by the appropriate State authority. Advancement to silk is not automatic.

County Courts Local courts formerly presided over by a County Court Judge and a Registrar but now by a Circuit judge and a District Judge. They have statutory civil jurisdictions.

Leader When Queen's Counsel is instructed in a case with a junior he or she is in charge of the running of the case and is called a leader.

Law Lords Full title is Lords of Appeal in Ordinary. Name given to the judges of the former final UK appellate court consisting of holders of high judicial office or barristers of at least fifteen years standing, who were appointed to life peerages under the Appellate Jurisdiction Act 1876 to carry out the judicial business of the House of Lords.

From 1st October 2009 jurisdiction was transferred to The Supreme Court of the United Kingdom, which has assumed the jurisdiction of the Privy Council and now constitutes the final UK court of appeal. Judges are called Justices of the Supreme Court and addressed as My Lord or My Lady.

Relocation is a short distance from The House of Lords to a new court in the Middlesex Guildhall, Parliament Square. Much controversy surrounded the question of whether the change was sensible or worthwhile given the enormous cost (estimated at between £78 and £100 million) and so little change of substance. At the changeover fees for bringing appeals or for seeking permission to appeal rose very significantly.

Magistrate A justice of the peace sitting in a magistrates' court. They are unpaid, without legal qualification and have power to try offences, which are triable summarily (broadly minor offences). They have too a licensing and a matrimonial jurisdiction as well as some administrative powers. In some large towns the volume of business requires full time magistrates. These are paid, legally qualified and known variously as stipendiary or metropolitan magistrates.

Modes of Address The proper mode of address to members of the tribunal in the Magistrates' Court is Sir or Madam as appropriate. 'Your Worship' is an expression much used but it is not correct. Your Honour is the proper form of address for judges (male and female) of the County and of the Crown Courts. In the High Court (all Divisions) the Court of Appeal, the House of Lords and from 1st October 2009 in The Supreme Court the proper form of address to a judge is My Lord or My Lady.

Quarter Sessions In relatively recent times a court presided over by magistrates with a legally qualified chairman. It was empowered to try indictable offences other than those triable only at assize. Quarter Sessions were abolished by the Courts Act 1971 and their jurisdiction is now exercised by the Crown Court.

Recorder A barrister or solicitor appointed under the Courts Act 1971 as a part time judge. They sit usually in the Crown Court and agree to make themselves available for not less than four weeks a year.

White wigs. References to 'white wigs'are to those who are new to the Bar, on account of youth or late entry and whose newly acquired wigs are accordingly (usually) clean and white.

The expression is used to describe those who may be inexperienced and/or nervous to be contrasted with the experienced old campaigners wearing their grey greasy (often scruffy) old wigs. The wearing of wigs in the civil courts was abolished in 2009.

'Shaggy Cap . . . Lawyer's Wig'.

PREFACE

As well as to entertain this book seeks to dispel a popular image of lawyers, variously that they are pedantic, pompous, humourless and above all avaricious (the last mentioned typified by Peter Brookes' delightful cartoon to be seen opposite).

Lawyers' Tales is a miscellany of law related stories and episodes. Entertaining, informative, occasionally tragic and sometimes very funny, they give some insight into how the law and the legal profession operate. Without any ordered sequence each tale comes as a surprise. They make easy reading and, it is hoped, portray lawyers as more human than many believe.

I have taken just a little material (varied slightly) from my previously published books. They however were primarily concerned with Latin and all (i.e., *Lawyers' Latin*, *Long Live Latin* and *Latin Today*) are substantially reference books likely only to be dipped into and seldom read from cover to cover.

For those without some familiarity with the law a few expressions may need explanation and a glance at pages xiii–xv above may be helpful. Further, a small number of tales may be too esoteric, likely to be understood only by those with some knowledge of the law: the great majority however, may be appreciated by all.

A few tales record old chestnuts. Those who have heard them before may enjoy reminder. I am pleased to pass them on to those who have not.

Creation of this book has involved approaches to many and in particular to senior and retired members of the legal profession for their recollections and generally. To a man they reacted with kindly enthusiasm to being bothered. I have to express my profound gratitude to Sir Michael Connell, Lord Saville of Newdigate, John Weeks QC (*quondam* Judge Weeks), Sir George Newman, John Crowley QC, Keith Topley (*quondam* Senior Master, Queen's Remembrancer and Admiralty Registrar), His

Honour Judge Coltart, Richard Gray QC, His Honour Judge Stephen Robbins, Jonathan Harvie QC, James Donovan, and Michael Oliver (my sometime barrister's clerks).

I am greatly indebted also to my wife Susie for her drawings of our animals and of fungi, to Tom Kemp and Julia Baxter for design of and lettering on the jacket, to Roger Lane, Patrick Phillips, Jeremy Metcalfe and Harry Frere, whose contributions from outside the profession have been invaluable; and to Ann Mansbridge and Tessa Papas each for gifting copyright permission in respect of drawings of Norman Mansbridge and William (Bill) Papas. To John Saunders for typesetting and overall invaluable production advice. Last but not least to my children Jonathon Gray, Theresa Kirkpatrick (née Gray) and Anna Gray for help generally in particular when my laptop computer misbehaved leaving me helpless.

John Gray 2010

'The mere title of lawyer is enough to deprive a man of public confidence.'
(Mark Twain) Peter Brookes

'Bow Street'. William Papas.

1. Teetotal

It is in the Magistrates'Courts (sometimes known as the Police Courts) that the majority of citizens are likely to encounter the law at work.

Circa 1962 a barrister, brisk and bustling, arrived in his Temple chambers one morning and announced to his pupil:

"I think that today you should take yourself to a Magistrates' Court: see what happens and get the feel of a place where you are initially, we hope, likely to get some work. Go to Bow Street."

Bow Street was a busy court and a short walk from The Temple. The pupil was astonished at the efficient speed of despatch of what might have seemed rough justice but for the charm of the Metropolitan Magistrate sitting alone (lay Magistrates sit in twos or threes).

A voice shouted "Michael O'Leary?"A dishevelled poor wretch appeared suddenly in the dock and a police officer came forward to prosecute and explained, after taking the oath:

"Michael O'Leary charged with being drunk and disorderly. Evening last I was on patrol duty in the Strand in company with PC Smith. Opposite Charing X Station the accused O'Leary came into our sight. He was shouting obscenities and lurching from side to side of the pavement and bumped to their inconvenience into two lawfully passing citizens before vomiting in the gutter. We were of the opinion that he was drunk, arrested him, detained him overnight in custody and this morning charged him with being drunk and disorderly".

Magistrate. "Thank you officer. Stand up O'Leary. Anything you want to say to me about this?"

"Yes I do your Worship."

"Very well go on, say it."

"Never a drap passed me lips."

"Anything more?"

"No your Worship."

"Very well. Case proved. Fined ten shillings (50p now but with a much diminished purchasing power) or one day's imprisonment in default. Off you go. Try not to do it again."

Dr. Crippen, Oscar Wilde and the Krays appeared before this court, which has been moved and, following planning permission, is probably to be converted into an hotel. The historic building is grade II listed.

2. Boredom

A youth entered the dock of a country Magistrates' Court. He wore a heavy leather jerkin, black and decorated with shiny silver-metal studs. He was accused of committing road traffic offences. His indifference to, indeed defiance of, the law was patent as he looked insolently about him chewing gum and shrugging his shoulders from time to time and answered 'guilty' to each of the charges put to him by a prosecuting police officer. There were so many. They had really thrown the book at him. No motor tax, no motor insurance, driving without due care and attention, speeding, no driving licence, bald tyres at insufficient pressure and a host of technical offences under the Construction and Use Regulations.

It was surprising that he had not managed to kill himself, let alone anybody else and it was all taking an intolerably long time as the officer turned solemnly the pages of his notebook and out-lined the facts relating to each charge.

The young man could bear it no longer. The effort of saying so often the word 'guilty' was plainly wearing him out. His attitude changed suddenly for the better, to one of eager helpful assistance to the court as he interrupted to announce:

"Your worships, I would not want to waste any more of the very valuable time of this honourable court. Look, you name it, I done it!"

3. Traffic Lights

Despite the exacting burden and standard of proof imposed by law upon the prosecution, acquittals in the Magistrates' Court are hard to come by. The word of any Tom, Dick or Harry just could not too often be preferred to that of police officers, who appear day in day out in the same court before the same magistrates. The system of 'justice' could break down.

Defendants usually need independent evidence if they are to stand a real chance of acquittal. Country solicitors, by reason of the size of their small community, feel acutely the above problem.

One such country solicitor acquired a client who had allegedly been seen by a police officer to have driven through a red traffic light. He denied this vehemently and he had an independent witness, who had signed a note to the effect that he had seen the incident in question and the traffic lights were not red or even amber as the accused's green Rover car passed through them.

The solicitor was quite excited at the prospect of putting one over the local police. At court the police officer testified to having seen the accused's green Rover car pass through the traffic lights, which were showing red against him as he did so. The accused gave evidence and hotly denied it, maintaining that at all material times the lights were green. Then came the independent witness. He looked a reliable enough kind of fellow aged about forty. In the witness box the solicitor questioned him with care, anxious to avoid any technical mishap. He established how he had become involved and that he was not a friend of the accused: then what he had seen.

"You saw the green Rover Car approach?"

"Yes."

"Did you see that car pass through the traffic lights?"

"Yes."

"Were the lights at any stage as the car passed through them at red as has been suggested?"

"No."

"Are you able to say whether or not the traffic lights were working?"

"I am and they were."

"Would you tell the court please what colour they were for the green Rover as it passed through them?"

As he asked this final question he was unable to conceal a certain anticipatory triumph in his voice.

"The lights were blue."

4. To sleep, to dream

A matrimonial dispute in the Magistrates' court can be very trying. Young counsel made his way to an outlandish Court to appear for a lady whose husband had allegedly treated her with cruelty. It was a hot and humid summers day. The proceedings started late and dragged on into the afternoon.

The bench was made up of three magistrates. The chairman, dressed in light tweeds, was a brusque individual, probably a retired army officer. He was flanked on one side by a younger, enthusiastic fellow and on the other by a middle aged lady bountiful adorned with twin set and pearls and wearing a modish wide brimmed hat.

Boredom with the case had already set in when the complainant lady-wife, when giving her evidence, declined to say in public the lewd and disgusting things with which her husband regularly regaled her at bedtime. This was all very tiresome and was protracting the tedious proceedings.

No amount of persuasion, cajolery or gentle threat from her counsel made any difference and she was not influenced by the Chairman's intervention to announce that he and his colleagues were unconcerned and had heard before the kind of things she hinted at. He spoke for the men for the smart lady had drifted into sleep concealed beneath her very large, elegant hat.

Then came the breakthrough. Why had nobody thought of it before? She would write it all down. The completed note, recording rich obscenities in remarkable (full marks for skill) combination and permutation, was read by both counsel, the younger man and the chairman. The faces of all showed the necessary suitable disapproval and disgust. The chairman turned to the elegant lady and, realising her inattention, nudged her gently out of deep slumber as he handed over the revealing note. She came to only slowly and, as her weary eyes focused suddenly on the content of the note: "Sir, have you taken leave of your senses?" She exclaimed, not sotto voce enough.

5. Threat

It is not only in the Magistrates' Court that witnesses will not give in evidence verbally from the witness box that which they have already said and had recorded in a written statement. So Lord Goddard (after he had retired as Lord Chief Justice) told in a speech given after a law dinner in Oxford in the late 1960s.

In a case presided over by him at the Old Bailey (The Central

Criminal Court), with some very bad and dangerous men in the dock, a vital lady witness declined to give the damning evidence expected of her: and as to which she had testified in a written and signed statement given to police.

Prosecuting counsel approached the problem from every angle and with the greatest care and tact. His Lordship talked of duty before venturing menace as gently as he could. All to no avail. Suddenly she relented, scribbled a note and handed it up to the judge. He read it.

"Madam" he said. "I too received only this very morning a like most blood curdling threatening letter. Sitting where I do at this moment dignity forbids that I should tell you what I did with it sitting in another place."

History does not relate whether and if so how she was thus persuaded to give the desired evidence.

6. Premature conviction?

Alarming episodes occur rarely in the courts but some are perhaps as amusing as they are dreadful.

A young barrister waiting for his own case to be heard (the waiting in Magistrates Courts is too often quite intolerable) once witnessed what follows. An elderly man was being tried for theft and acted in person. The moustached chairman of three Magistrates was clearly getting very bored and had become somewhat tetchy.

There came a time when the accused announced that he would like to call a witness supportive of his version of events. The lady usher was an intolerable time outside court trying to find the named witness. A foreign name had evidently caused confusion but the man was eventually found and brought into court.

The chairman had in all this time fallen into what was either a deep sleep, a coma or some kind of trance. Emerging slowly back into the world of the living, he evidently experienced still some confusion and imagined that something was expected of him. So he obliged and uttered those so familiar words that come so easily to every Magistrate, so depressing for every defending advocate: "we find the case proved." This bombshell caused some consternation all round. A long and ugly silence followed before the clerk of the court intervened to save the day. Sitting in front of the magistrates, he wagged an admonitory finger and advised authoritatively loud and clear: "Not yet!"

7. Smoked Salmon

The gentle humour of an undergraduate, who years later rose to high judicial office, is well remembered. At a beginning of term tutorial undergraduates sat around a long oak table awaiting arrival of their teaching don to give a briefing as to what would be the content of tutorials in the following weeks. He arrived only moments late and, as he sat down, announced that this term they would be learning about the law of torts. He waved a green textbook, which they would be using and advised acquisition of a copy. It was called *Salmond on Torts*, he announced for the benefit of those furthest away at the other end of the table: not perhaps sufficiently loudly for some. "What's that about salmon on toast?" asked an inquiring voice, not wholly appreciated.

8. Judicium parium*

In December 1959 two letters appeared in the correspondence columns of the Oxford Mail. One came from Brasenose College deploring the more than usually juvenile behaviour of some of its undergraduate members.

The other praised nothing more than youthful ebullience. "It was good to know that the spirit of the College lives on . . . . I was up in 1899."

What had happened?

Over lunchtime beer in The King's Arms a small group of Brasenose undergraduates had noticed the fresh faced young men/boys milling around the college up for entry and/or scholarship interview. "Why don't we interview them?" ventured one idly. The mischievous idea however, as a hugely amusing jape, advanced very quickly to reality.

With the connivance of the porter they posted a notice summoning all candidates to the College law library for interview that evening. The jokers acquired long scholar's gowns and rearranged the law library, which consisted of two rooms, to facilitate interviewing. One borrowed a white coat from his scout, so that he could pose as a psychiatrist sitting on his own at a desk separate from the main body of interviewers. No don evidently saw the notice and 65 eager but nervous looking hopefuls duly appeared at the appointed time.

The interview panel comprised six members and was chaired by a budding lawyer. All had done national service and looked just that little bit older: sufficient not to be suspect.

The chairman stood up and informed the candidates that he held the invidious position of Moral Tutor to the College. He introduced the panel, two professors, teachers of law (one an

---

* Judicium parium 'judgement of peers or equals'. From Magna Carta.

imaginary but impressive sometime rowing blue!) the Junior Dean; two doctors, one a lecturer in English, the other the College psychiatrist.

Everyone was interviewed by about 10.45 p.m., initially one at a time but later in fours so as to get through the business.

History relates very little of the interviews' content. Straight faces were maintained and nobody guessed that it was a set up. One question asked was: 'what are your views on the conflict between sin and faith, in particular the carnal variety as portrayed in the novels of Graham Greene?" No answer is recorded. Those whose answers were naïve or unworldly were immediately directed to the psychiatrist. One line of questioning was used more than once: a version is recorded:

"You are from a public school, mainly boarders?"

"Yes Sir."

"No girls?"

"No Sir. I mean there are no girls."

"You know that there are girls in ladies' colleges in this university, but not here in Brasenose?"

"Yes Sir."

"You realise that they would attend the same lectures as you?"

"Yes Sir."

"Will you speak to them?"

"Yes Sir, I think so. A little perhaps."

"Will you invite them to come out with you?"

"Yes Sir. I think so." (A little hesitantly).

"And if they agree to go out with you, will you take them?"

"Yes Sir." Enthusiastically.

"And when you take them out, what will you do to them?"

Red faces, no answers and immediate assignment to the psychiatrist.

The candidates were soon after informed of the truth, told not to worry and wished the best of luck with their official interviews. For the most part this seemed to be taken in good heart.

The letters to the Oxford Mail had been spoof, written by the hoaxers.

No disciplinary action was taken. The Senior Dean at the time (one Robert Shackleton, an immensely likeable and very eccentric character with a sense of humour) to whose notice this irregularity came, evidently did not regard it as very serious and reputedly observed: "after all their behaviour did no appreciable damage to the college fabric."

But what, the reader may ask, has this original, inspired and larger than life episode got to do with 'Lawyers' Tales'? Well only that of those involved four read law and, in the fullness of time, two held judicial office and of these one rose to the very top of the legal tree, to be a Lord of Appeal in Ordinary and latterly a Justice of the Supreme Court.

9. *Fascinating law*

It is from that very early pupillage time that the young impressionable barrister remembers so much. At such a time a pupil was sent to listen to an appeal in a Rent Act case to be conducted, not by his pupil master, but by another senior member of the chambers (Mr W.A.B. Forbes). The pupil knew nothing of the Rent Act law (it had formed no part of the university or Bar Examination syllabus). The proceedings before three Lords Justices of Appeal were very technical, dry and dull. It was hard indeed to remain awake.

When it was all over, as he walked back with Mr Forbes to chambers across the zebra crossing in front of the Royal Courts of Justice, they chatted.

"Well now, young man, did you stay awake?" he asked with a grin in his broad Scottish accent.

"If I'm honest I fear that sleep accounted for quite a lot of what I do not remember."

"It is as well that you should learn early that much of the law can only be described as bloody boring. But it's like war. You cannot afford to go to sleep because that is when you get blown up. Amazing how often some vital piece of evidence, fact or matter crops up and is missed by counsel who has become comatose with boredom or has gone to sleep. Yes, young man, it is as well to stay awake in court. It is another matter if the judge nods off. Somebody has to waken him or her, particularly if snoring. But judges are not to be blamed for any small slip or error, after all; *aliquando dormitat bonus Homerus* 'even good Homer sometimes nods off.'" Horace. Ars Poetica, 359.

10. Virility

A pupil was engaged to take a note in one of his master's cases. He was separately instructed and to be paid! . . . a small fee (in guineas as was the custom then: a guinea being twenty one shillings or £1.05 post decimalisation). At lunchtime the court adjourned and he accompanied his master back to their Inn of Court for lunch. There he was sat amongst his master's senior colleagues. They talked shop.

"I should be pleased to have your view on a matter which has been exercising my mind. A most unfortunate personal injury matter. The plaintiff, my client, has received terrible multiple injuries having been struck by a swinging crane. The quantum of his damages is the only issue. I have sought to arrive at a figure by assessing a sum for damages attracted by each injury separately, adding them together and then discounting appropriately the overall total. There is internal abdominal injury, two broken femurs and permanent impotence in a man of 39. I can find no guiding authority for that last mentioned unhappy affliction in isolation. You do plenty of personal injury work. What do you think?"

The great man (so many pupils regard their master as a great man . . . or lady and hang on his/her every word) continued to chew a mouthful of his lunch with solemn thinking furrowed brow, giving deep thought to this grave and weighty matter.

"Five million pounds!"

"Yes, I was hoping for your helpful objective professional opinion, not this startling personal revelation."

11. Spanish Interlude

The newly qualified barrister is able to say 'I'm loose on the public now' and to comfort himself with the thought that any blunders he may make can, unlike the doctors, be put right by a higher court and by the expenditure of mere money. The new common law barrister may however often find his aspirations to things that really mattter postponed as he discovers himself instructed to defend endless cases of driving without due care and attention (careless driving). Very depressing as he trails out, for very modest remuneration, to outlandish magistrates' courts: hot and dusty in summer, cold and wet in winter, to be faced with magistrates who seem to have forgotten how difficult the standard and burden of proof ought to make it to convict one who in law is presumed innocent until proved guilty. Too regular repetition by these tribunals of the incantation 'we find the case proved' leaves him depressed and with a lamentable success rate. His most eloquent and cogent submissions seem to be as so much water off a duck's back and to make not the slightest difference. A good honours law degree is utterly wasted. Nothing glamorous about the job.

Too regular a diet of careless driving cases could break his spirit he begins to think. He has to take a break. That is how one, now retired, but once newly qualified, (i.e., called to the Bar, pupillage completed and something over a year in practice) recollects. Easter approached. He would go to Spain, to Madrid. Franco ruled and only recently had a visa become unnecessary. Iberia took him to foreign parts hitherto denied to a wartime generation.

At Barahas airport the Guardia Civil seemed to be everywhere: they were swarthy, looked ferocious and carried guns! He spoke no Spanish but hoped to meet up with a young Spanish woman he knew, who lived in Madrid and who had worked with the Spanish commercial attaché in London. Contacted by phone she revealed that she had a free week and would show him around. Wonderful, away from 'careless drivings' for seven whole days!

It was a restorative week. Bright clear sun by day and bitter chill at night. She drove him everywhere and in those few days he became acquainted with so much of enchanting historic Spain. The Alcazar, the Roman aqueduct at Segovia, Toledo, the mediaeval walled city of Avila, the amazing Valley of the Fallen and King Philip II's magnificent Escorial with lunch there at the Hotel Felipe Secundo.

On the last day she announced "before you go home, you are *abogado*, you have to see the Palacio de Justicia (pronounced *hoostithia* . . . accordingly, being linguistically inadequate, he wasn't immediately sure what he had to see). The guide was good company, pretty and determined, so they went.

Inside the *Palacio* was a remarkable scene, a positive imbroglio in which a lot of individuals were talking animatedly at the same time. A man wearing a black gown, apparently the judge, sat expressionless and looked indifferently on: our Englishman assumed because the outcome in a prosecution of some dissident Franco opponent was foregone but asked his interpreter guide notwithstanding what it was all about.

"They say that he drive imprudently. He say that he don't."
Déjà vu.

12. Naughty

Lord Hailsham, when he was Lord Chancellor, made no secret of the fact that, when sitting on the woolsack in the House of Lords, it was frequently his habit to mutter "bollocks", sotto voce "to the bishops!" This man was a fellow of All Souls College, Oxford and head of the judiciary. We don't know and can only guess at what awfulness (or forgiveness!) the bishops might in return have been muttering about the Lord Chancellor.

His barrister son, Douglas Hogg, hit the headlines in June 2009 with his claim as an MP to very substantial Parliamentery expenses for having the moat cleared at his Lincolnshire manor house.

13. Seconds out of the ring

The legendary FE Smith ('FE', later Lord Birkenhead) was once engaged in a case where a jockey, who had failed to weigh in after a race, left the witness box prematurely, after examination in chief, so as to deny FE the opportunity to cross-examine. He was quickly invited to return: Mr Justice Darling observing darkly: "Mr Smith has not weighed in yet."

FE is however renowned for his own responses. His capacity to throw a knockout verbal counter-punch was without equal. On one famous occasion it is said (apocryphally perhaps) that, in a case, which he had just opened, the judge sneeringly observed:

"I have heard all that you have had to say, Mr Smith, but fear that I am none the wiser."

"Possibly not My Lord, but a lot better informed just the same."
FE's potential for lightning waspish retort was just as evident

outside the law. On an electoral platform he watched a man heckle one on whose behalf he had just spoken. Moved suddenly by indignation, FE suggested to this man that he might like to take off his cap when addressing a question.

"I'll take off my boots if you like" said the man.

"Ah, I knew you had come to be unpleasant" replied FE.

FE was not the only one noted for instant return with interest of anything in the nature of a judicial jibe. So it is said (apocryphally perhaps) that a judge complained to Sir Andrew Clark (then Mr):

"I am getting a little weary of your gems of Chancery learning."

He could hardly have expected the esoteric and barbed boomerang retort:

"I would be grateful notwithstanding if Your Lordship would bear with me for a few moments longer. I am about to cast my last pearl."

14. Begorra

"Away with him, away with him! He speaks Latin." Shakespeare. Henry vi, II. Act iv. sc.7.

In recent years (since early 1999) the use of Latin in the law has undergone a persecution. One expression however has survived as much among laymen as lawyers. The former seem to enjoy a smattering of the law's eccentricity rooted in antiquity. . . *Res ipsa loquitur* (the thing itself speaks or the thing speaks for itself) is an example. Probably it is based on Cicero (Pro Milone 53) '*Res loquitur ipsa quae semper valeant plurimum*' the fact speaks for itself and that is always of the utmost value. In the law the words have come to serve as a label for a somewhat esoteric and technical application of a shifting burden of proof in accident cases. Explanation is not appropriate here (for explanation See John

Gray's *Lawyers' Latin* new edition at pages 119–120).

Inclusion here is however permissible and germane by reason of an old story told of a well-known nineteenth/twentieth century Irish barrister, Serjeant Sullivan, who practised in later life in England. A judge opined: "This would appear to me to be a case for application of the maxim *res ipsa loquitur*. Is that an expression with which you are familiar Mr Sullivan?"

The question was offensive. The expression was basic law and of course Sullivan was familiar with that well-known Latin maxim. He gave as good as he got.

"Why my Lord, I am indeed, very familiar: in the vales of southern Ireland, whence I hail, the people talk of little else."

15. Schooldays again

A newly appointed Recorder sat with two lay magistrates hearing appeals from the Magistrates' Court. One of the magistrates was a headmaster. A matter arose which involved a point of law. "Oh" said the Recorder "this I'm afraid is down to me. We can adjourn overnight. I will look up the law and produce a written answer by the morning."

Next morning the members of the tribunal met.

"Have you written the answer to what is *our* legal problem?" asked the headmaster. The Recorder answered in the affirmative.

"May I see what you have written on our behalf?" the teacher went on.

"Yes of course" said the Recorder, covered in confusion at his unthinking neglect and want of courtesy and instantly handing over his manuscript. "Very interesting" said the headmaster after a little "grammar and punctuation could be improved."

16. Difficult Law

A young Chancery Barrister made his way burdened with heavy legal textbooks and reports (a wearing inconvenience largely eliminated by the advent of the photocopier) to the Amersham County Court in days when it was presided over by the inimitable and unpredictable Judge Claude Duveen, a man of decision (sometimes eccentric, sometimes outrageous) strong in personality.

Counsel for the plaintiff (claimant) opened the case to him at length uninterrupted and finished with the observation that "it could be seen that the case raised difficult questions of law and in particular of quasi-estoppel, which would have to be considered in some detail." "Not in Amersham they won't. We're concerned only with the facts in this court and I find them" retorted the judge.

17. Hearing aid

Counsel's visit to another County court was disconcerting. He commenced opening of his case. Softly spoken as counsel go, he was not surprised after a little to be asked by the judge to speak up: "I can't hear you." Counsel apologised and duly raised his voice. "I still can't hear you," said the judge manifesting signs of incipient irritation. Counsel resorted to a shout. "Oh dear, just wait a moment," said the judge, twiddling with some technology in his right ear. "Try again" he asked at length. Counsel responded with a shout that he feared he might not be able to maintain for the duration of the case. He need not have worried. "Oh dear oh dear" said the judge "very well just carry on."

18. Needing glasses?

In a London criminal court a convicted man was asked whether there was anything he would like to say before sentence was passed. "Fuck all", said the man with an offensive defiance not unusually encountered from criminals in the dock. "I didn't catch that" said the judge addressing the clerk. "Fuck all", said the clerk. "Funny" said the judge. "I thought I saw his lips move."

19. Paucis verbis*

At the old London Quarter Sessions sat a judge, who had become weary of the petty criminals who came endlessly before him, and who had a tendency to ferocity. But he was smiling, had a sense of humour and was kind to white wigs. His name was Reginald Seaton (Reggie). He was a large man and sat on a dais high up above his court 1. The writer, a white wig at the time, felt some trepidation as he waited for his case to be called on and witnessed an unrepresented defendant's case dealt with. In that matter the defendant was evidently of Greek origin aptly named 'Unscrupoulos' and wore a scruffy brown suit. He had declined legal aid and the assistance of counsel having earlier pleaded guilty to various frauds and theft of an awful lot of bathroom equipment from a builder's yard. Prosecuting counsel outlined the facts.

"Anything you dispute or would like to say?" asked the judge.

"No. Fucking waste of fucking time"came the response in an aggressively sullen voice of defiant hostility.

Prosecuting counsel called the police officer to prove the

* Paucis verbis 'with few words'.

antecedents (namely his criminal record, if any, and a short rundown on what was known about his background). The extent of his past criminality was a surprise to the young waiting barrister, whose task later in the day was to defend an alleged shoplifter who was of previous good character and had done no more than 'take' a Mars Bar.

"Anything you would like to ask the police officer?" said the judge.

"No" replied the prisoner without his previous vernacular embellishment.

"Anything you dispute?"

"No."

Anything you would like to say to me before I sentence you?"

"No."

"Very well, not much to say to you either. Three years."

20. Cliché

An abrupt ending to a case is attributed to Mr Justice Avory. It is very well known but could notwithstanding scarcely be omitted from a work of this nature. A convicted man stood up to be sentenced by him then opened his mouth to announce:

"As God is my judge, I am not guilty of these offences."

"He is not, I am, you are, three years imprisonment" answered His Lordship.

21. Undiplomatic

In 1967 the breathaliser effectively succeeded the old unsatisfactory law whereby there was only one drink-drive offence, 'driving whilst unfit through drink or drugs'. Often hard to prove it resulted in jury acquittals of hard drinkers, who maintained that they had developed a tolerance and could and did drive perfectly safely and quite fit with body alcohol levels which might explode the new breathalyser.

Awaiting his turn in a Magistrates' Court a young barrister was interested to watch the progress of a prosecution under the new law. A plea of guilty was entered and none of the legal technical subtleties later to make appearance was raised. The accused was well dressed and spoken, an accountant by profession.

A police officer told the story as recorded in his notebook. Near midnight on the day in question he had been on duty with another officer in a marked police car when they had their attention drawn to a Mercedes car being driven erratically and at high speed. They gave chase and it was some chase, at speed with blue light flashing and, despite the late hour, gong sounding. Eventually the driver yielded and the car screeched to a halt.

"I approached the car and found there to be only a male driver. From the manner of his driving we were of the opinion that he may have been drinking. His window was tight shut. I invited him to open it and informed him that we would like him to take a breathalyser test. The driver did not wind the window down and he did not speak."

The officer relied heavily on his notebook as he went on:

"I then knocked on his window. He did not open it and looked the other way. I knocked again, this time very hard, on the window, which he did then open. There was a strong smell of alcohol and I saw that his eyes were glazed. I informed him yet again that we required him to take a breathalyser test. The defendant did then speak. He said . . . ." There was a pregnant pause as he turned over yet another page of his notebook. "Officer, why don't you just fuck off?"

That moment of defiant glory cost him dear.

'Ban the breath test!'

. . . "Ban the Breath Test," Norman Mansbridge

22. Rare manuscript

There are ways other than use of offensive language in which those who feel aggrieved can manifest feelings of resentful discontent with the administration of justice. A farmer with a burning sense of injustice appealed to the Buckinghamshire Quarter Sessions against a conviction by the Aylesbury Magistrates for careless driving. Sitting as Chairman of Sessions was Lord Justice Arthian Davies, known as 'Beetle', a man slow to suffer fools gladly. He bustled into court flanked by two magistrates. Irritation showed in his glowering countenance and all bowed before sitting down. Counsel feared a rough ride before him as he put on one of a selection of his glasses.

"I appear for the crown in this matter," said prosecuting counsel rising to his feet to deal with the first case called.

"A moment Mr er, er . . ." said the chairman as he searched for the note of counsel's name, which the clerk should have provided.

" . . . Mr Jones. I can't find the notice of appeal."

"I can let you Sir, have a look at my copy but it is hard to read. May I respectfully suggest that you Sir have another look . . ."

The implicit suggestion of incompetence worsened further the chairman's glowering countenance.

" . . . for the document in question is unusual and not perhaps in the anticipated regular form for which I am sure you are looking . . . ."

"Got on, tell me why."

"It appears to reflect his feelings towards the administration of justice . . ."

"Well?"

"It is hand written upon a piece of Izal toilet tissue."

23. Anonymity

In AD 2008 it was decreed that in England and Wales wigs should no longer be worn by barristers or judges in the civil courts. Remarkable apparel, they had managed for centuries to grace and give a curious gravitas to the Bar. White and clean, when new they usually identified a newcomer, young and short on experience, but enthusiastic and ambitious. Greasy, shabby and grey in colour they were likely to indicate a veteran campaigner, his true abilities belied by the often appalling state of his wig. Small wonder that an edible species of fungi, scruffy in appearance, is called 'Shaggy Cap. Lawyer's Wig' (*coprinus comatus*).

The wearing of wigs has however been retained in the criminal courts where they provide a valuable anonymity for judge and counsel. A recorder sitting in a Crown Court acquired real insight into lay views of the case he tried. He had left his sandwich lunch at home and ventured into a nearby pub to buy some. Without his wig, and having removed his tabs with wing collar and re-instated a conventional collar and tie, he went unrecognised and, as he waited in a queue, spotted in front of him two jurymen a snatch of whose conversation he overheard. They disobeyed his direction not yet to discuss the case and one's approach astounded him. "We don't need to listen to all this evidence: wasting all this time. An inner mechanism tells me who is guilty."

'Shaggy Cap and Lawyer's Wig.' Susan Gray

Behind him, in the same queue were two men he recognised from the members of the public sitting at the rear of the court. Evidently they were distinctly unimpressed by counsel. Said one in his northern accent "that there prosecuting barrister is just like Rumpole of Bailey,"

"If you ask me" said his companion "I reckon just same that the accused's got no chance; he's got arsehole of Bailey."

Without wigs what profound insights might we miss?!

24. Fiat Justitia*

Throughout his remarkable judicial career, spanning 38 years, Lord Denning became famous for 'looking to the merits.' His approach had been to consider what was fair between the contestants, how well or badly they had each behaved in the transaction under consideration and generally which party was the more deserving. He would then proceed, as far as he could, to mould the law so as to reach what he adjudged to be the just result. There were those who thought that, in his early days as a judge at least, too often he found more flexibility in the law than many considered existed. Much academic controversy centred round the quasi-estoppel introduced by his decision in Central London Property Trust Ltd. v High Trees House Ltd., [1947] K.B. 130.

As motto for his coat of arms, not surprisingly, he took *fiat justitia* – 'let justice be done.' Unknown to him at the time, and quite a shock when he discovered it, is the origin of that expression to be found in Seneca the younger (1 Dialogues, III, 18). Piso (a Roman official) ordered a centurion to carry out sentence of death on a soldier for murder of one Gaius, but before execution Gaius turned up, alive! Piso's reaction was to say "*fiat justitia . . .*" and

* Fiat justitia 'let justice be done'.

24

order the deaths of the soldier because his sentence stood, the centurion for failing to obey orders and Gaius for causing the death of two innocent men.

Lord Denning retired in 1982 at the age of 83.

He was greatly amused, when appointed Master of the Rolls, to receive a letter from the owner of a Rolls Royce car in America congratulating him on becoming 'Master of the Rolls Royce.'

A Crown Court judge was recently asked if he operated on Denning principles. "More or less" he replied "we still assess the relevant qualities of the parties involved but there is an up-date. The exercise is known as 'who is the greater shit principle.'"

25. Jungle justice

In the 1960s, despatching judicial business in England were a few of those who had returned from a fast shrinking British Empire. 'Jungle judges'as they were known. Civilisation had moved on faster at home than on the whole in the outposts of Empire and the justice they meted out was seen sometimes to have a certain jungular quality about it. At Quarter Sessions one such judge was seen to work himself into a fury as he thumbed endlessly through the Larceny Act 1916 before, finally exasperated, announcing that he couldn't find the flogging section.

'Jungle Justice' Norman Mansbridge

26. Ignorance is bliss

A senior junior common law barrister received instructions to advise in a complicated commercial matter. The client wanted counsel's written opinion. The matter embraced several aspects of the law and took a very long time only partially to produce. There emerged a company law problem to which, try as he would, he could find no answer in the textbooks or cases and, it being outside his field of expertise, he felt uneasy about venturing his own view.

It troubled him. He needed the help of a specialist company lawyer. His solicitor agreed that one be instructed: not without hesitation for the extra expense was considerable. A learned Chancery company law expert was duly involved. After a short time he telephoned to explain that after much thought and research he didn't know the answer either. They wrote a joint opinion which, wrapped up as much as possible, came undeniably in the last analysis to nothing more or less than (on the point in question) "we don't know." Counsel's costly opinion!

27. Contributory negligence

In his early days at the Bar a barrister, who later rose to the High Court Bench, was briefed to defend a mugger who, so the prosecution alleged, had behaved like a latter day 'Dick Turpin' highway robber. The evidence against his client was strong and good, indeed overwhelming. This was pointed out to the accused and it was suggested to him that he might like to consider a plea of guilty; it could be to his advantage when it came to sentence. But no, he would have none of it. He was not guilty and was ready for a contest.

Counsel accepted the challenge and, as he was professionally bound to do, did his very best as an advocate with perfectly hopeless material, a very wearing and exhausting exercise, but a necessary one. It is not for counsel to form an opinion, decide guilt and decline his services when an accused maintains innocence. A person framed might never be professionally defended.

After three days of torment, inviting the jury seriously to accept the absurd and that black is white and vice versa, a verdict of guilty was brought in. With due solemnity the judge read a little homily deploring this increasingly prevalent offence, which used to be committed on lonely highways at night by men on horseback with black masks and flint lock pistols appearing out of dark forests: men who were hanged for their iniquity if and when run to ground by the Bow Street Runners. He then imposed a sentence of five years imprisonment upon one who had done it before, more than once.

Some weeks later counsel received in the post a small brown envelope addressed to him in manuscript. Inside he found a note on official paper, evidently from his erstwhile client now in H.M. Prison Pentonville. It bore a succinct message. 'Dear Mr . . . . . ., I know it's not **all** your fault that things went so badly and I got five years but can **we** do anything about it?'

'A sentence of five years imprisonment'

Norman Mansbridge

28. Pro bono

There must be few, if any, practising barristers (or indeed judges or retired barristers) around in AD 2010 who received or even remember a Dock Brief. Many perhaps don't know what it was or what it entailed. It was a system of legal representation by members of the Bar for the benefit of those indicted and without sufficient means to fund their defence: the professional gentleman's contribution to society. By the 1960s it was not quite free. No alleged criminal was entitled to Counsel's assistance unless he was worth £2 four shillings and six (old) pence (£2.23p. post decimalisation) and had first paid it to counsel. It was a breach of etiquette and unprofessional for counsel to appear on behalf of one afforded a dock brief unless first paid this sum of money. 'Dock brief' was exactly that: brief to counsel direct from the accused in the dock without the intervention of a solicitor.

The entry in many dictionaries of law is very short and uninformative, giving no idea of how one received a dock brief and what this might mean to the recipient. A slightly varied version of one barrister's recollection will serve to explain the procedure and why the possibility of receiving such a brief was a perpetual discomfiting threat hanging over the head of every junior barrister who ventured into the higher criminal courts.

'I travelled to Nottingham to appear on a plea of guilty for a nasty stabbing. On reaching the court I robed up, saw my unattractive client and went into the courtroom. The benches bristled with counsel already assembled for pleas and applications. Within moments the judge appeared and whispered something to the clerk, who then announced: 'Dock Briefs.' There was no escape. It was unprofessional to leave the courtroom.

The first accused was called up from the dungeons below and appeared in the dock flanked by two prison warders: a skinny sad looking fellow. After determining that he was worth £2 four shillings and six pence, the clerk invited him to select any barrister present to represent him simply by pointing with his finger. My God, I thought, should he pick me I could be really in it if he pleads not guilty and keeps me here for a couple of days or more. I'd have to pay a hotel, another train fare and return the next day's hoped for unusually remunerative case, enough to pay the chambers rent for a month.

Times were hard in the early days at the Bar and to lose the next day's prospective case would be a disaster of very large proportions. He might however not pick me: mine was a very white wig and I was sure that to an old lag (which, knowing nothing of him, monstrously I assumed him to be) like him would mean inexperience to be avoided. There was too a certain safety in numbers, at least a dozen barristers from whom to choose. And, even if he did choose me, every chance that he might plead guilty. While these horror thoughts flashed through my mind the prisoner was eyeing counsel and deciding at whom he would point his finger. These were anxious moments and I held my breath, lowered my head (eye contact was to be avoided) and hoped for the best.

Relief. He chose another. The smoothest of men, who typified himself by the prominence of an enormous gold signet ring on the little finger of his left hand, rose grandly to his feet with slow affectation, before announcing:

"It is with the greatest respect and regret that I must decline. I hold brief for the prosecution in this very matter."

Anxiety exploded inside me. I was back in the arena. From the dock the accused eyed interminably each one of the remaining cohort of reluctant counsel. At any moment he would raise and point the finger of fate: and with sudden decision he did and the finger pointed indisputably at me. I was numb with horror.

In the cells below I met my new client. I explained my predicament and felt embarrassed in extracting my fee of £2 four shillings and six pence. He was a man of real charm but who had done it too often before, stealing garden gnomes! He found them irresistible

29

but relieved my tension: he would plead guilty. They had him, he said, 'bang to rights'. I was more familiar with 'it's a fair cop guv'nor.'

Conflicting versions of 'the gospel truth' were hard to reconcile but we got there in the end and he was pleased to be given only nine months. Having disposed of my other matter, I did not have to return my remunerative brief, which did materialise for the next day. I had however found the whole episode very stressful.

Of my dock brief fee the four and sixpence was due to my clerk. I thought the remaining £2 to be potentially lucky and sought hopefully to increment my derisory fee by buying two of the recently introduced premium bonds with the actual notes, but they never won (or not yet).'

The dock brief fell into disuse in the later 1960s with the advance of legal aid.

29. Statutory interpretation

A number of Latin phrases have developed into rules of law. They are expressed in the Latin of antiquity as a shorthand, and are (or used to be) used to govern the interpretation of documents and Statutes e.g., the *contra proferentem* rule (meaning 'against the [party] proferring).' Thus where there is uncertainty or ambiguity in a document, it will be construed against the party proferring it, who is responsible for its production and content and must bear the adverse consequences of any deficiency in meaning or otherwise. There are several other such rules, *ejusdem generis*, *noscitur a sociis* etc ('of the same type' and 'it is known from fellows or allies'). They will be familiar to lawyers but the fact that they are not here explained is because that would be lengthy (and largely irrelevant) and is perhaps one reason why they have come to be encapsulated in succinct Latin, used as a label.

Invocation of one or more of these Latin rules is however not always of any assistance whatsoever. So as not to baffle those who find it necessary to read them, statutes often include a 'simple' explanatory 'for the avoidance of doubt' section. One such provision purports to render more comprehensible part of the Road Transport Lighting Act 1967. Lawyers of many ages had it drawn to their attention in an after dinner speech given by Lord Justice Eveleigh in Oxford in the 1970s. Manifesting some personal amusement he emphasised that it was an 'avoidance of doubt' provision and read it to the assembled company.

'It is hereby declared for the avoidance of doubt that material designed primarily to reflect white light as light of that or another colour is, when reflecting light, to be treated for the purposes of the principal Act as showing a light and material capable of reflecting an image is not, when reflecting the image of a light, to be so treated.'

The Lord Justice drew attention to the presence among the company of a much esteemed professor of law, to whom he had read the provision before. He however made no apology for repetition, declaring that he would continue to repeat it until such time as the latter claimed to understand it.

30. Remuneration

One winters night a barrister awoke to the sound of fast dripping water. The weather had been freezing and, though it was warmer now, it was sufficiently cold still for him to be reluctant to get out of bed and inspect. What a good thing he did. The kitchen had been flooded by what was almost certainly a burst pipe, which had been frozen. But it was not apparent where it was. He could cut off the water supply by tying up the ball-cock in the attic tank, but that would mean no shaving (and he had conferences next day), no tea for breakfast and worst of all a ban on pulling the chain in the lavatory. His wife and children managed to sleep through all this.

There was nothing for it but to call a plumber immediately. This was done. He arrived post haste. He knew his job. Shut off the water, traced the leak (a pipe which had indeed been frozen and thawed) fixed it and lagged it properly: all very quickly.

"Thank you so much", said the barrister "I can't tell you how grateful I am. Let me settle up. Tell me how much I owe and I'll write you a cheque right now."

"£700", said the plumber.

Silence. The barrister gasped.

" Surely not. That seems a bit steep to me. What is your hourly rate?"

"£350. I've taken two hours inclusive of travelling time."

"That is far more than twice my own rate. I'm a barrister and charge £125 per hour."

"Much the same as I charged when I was a barrister."

A story with perhaps some reality for young barristers practising crime: given Gordon Brown's government's attitude to the funding of criminal legal aid in 2009–2010.

31. Indecision

Probation Officers produce social inquiry reports for judges to see the background to the commission of crime and hence to assess a convicted person and take into account in deciding what might be an appropriate sentence. These reports frequently tend to kindness, looking idealistically to rehabilitation, and often make unrealistic proposals largely ignoring the punitive and deterrent element usually necessary in sentencing. One such report was long, detailed and thoughtful. It concluded that the convicted man was schizophrenic. The officer declared himself 'in two minds' as to what might be the right course. It left the judge with two unrealistic proposals.

32. Light interlude

November 1945 saw the Nuremberg trials of most of Hitler's Nazi leaders. In the dock sat, *inter alios*, Hermann Goering with just the trace of a smug smile on his face, Von Ribbentrop (the aloof diplomat, nose in the air, oozing disdain and denying the court's jursdiction: known to the British foreign office as 'Von Brickendrop') and Hess, who read a book and took no interest in the proceedings around him.

These men faced accusations of crimes as dreadful as the world has ever seen and the prospect of the gallows. Every word of the lengthy indictment was read out in soulless tones. Amongst so many much more serious counts in the indictment, Goering was charged with plundering from France many works of art and other desirable articles. For plunder of 87 million bottles of champagne he showed no remorse as it brought memory of better times and a broad smile to his face.

33. Terrible smell

A London branch of a retail chain of stores was suddenly struck by the most terrible of unanticipated disasters. The downstairs lavatory overflowed but not gently. Explosive forces unknown blasted the most unattractive of substances with great force out of the ceramic pan to splat against the ceiling, whence it dripped back down to the ground. Worse still this kept on happening without any warning, so that staff were terrified of entering the room either to satisfy nature's call or to attempt clean up. It was a 'no-go zone' of which one witness testified: "the very idea of going into that room scared the living daylights out of me."

Managers were convinced that the cause of this horrific phenomenon was some malfunction in a government sewage works not far away but they received no admission from senior officials of the latter, who showed little interest in relieving the plight of the afflicted. Customers seldom ventured much beyond the door of entry before retreating hastily back to fresh air outside. Staff were overcome. Something had to be done. But what? Go to law.

At a conference they received advice from counsel to the effect that they could not just serve an injunction on the sewage works restraining them by their servants or agents from doing all things causative of the trouble complained of; quite apart from the fact that no judge would grant an injunction in such terms.

"To secure a mandatory injunction you need to tell them exactly what they are to stop doing," said counsel. "Furthermore I am afraid to have to tell you that in law there is no entitlement to such an injunction against a government department."

Decisive men decided to threaten injunction proceedings for what they were worth. First an expert would have to be instructed to explain the problem and exactly what steps it would be necessary to take to put things right.

Shortly after the management team came to meet again with Counsel. They had engaged an expert who had examined the suspect premises and all plant and machinery on it. He came direct to the conference. Speed was vital. He apologised.

"I have not yet had opportunity to write up my report."

"No matter" replied counsel. "You have been wonderfully quick and I am sure that all concerned are very grateful. Please, for the moment, just explain to us what is the problem so that we can direct those responsible as to exactly what they are to do and/or stop doing to bring this appalling state of affairs to an end: and, if there be more, what needs to be done to put it permanently right?" asked counsel.

"I just don't know" he replied.

History does not relate more.

34. Supremacy

It is well known to lawyers that in most sets of barrister's chambers the clerk reigns (or did in times past) supreme. That his pre-eminence is known outside the profession is confirmed by an unhappy incident that befell a set in the Temple. The ceramic, after the design of that famous engineer, Thomas Crapper, failed to operate as a disposal unit with terrible consequences and embarrassment for chambers. The senior clerk was put in charge of remedial operations. A plumber was summoned post haste and arrived with drain rods and other specialist equipment. It did not take him very long to restore effective function. Overheard was part of a conversation between the plumber and the clerk as the latter effected payment.

"Tell me your diagnosis?"

"Well I don't rightly know. The unit has a four inch outlet pipe. I can only think that one of your governors has a really terrible problem."

A more refined breed, the clerk and his entourage were apparently wholly above suspicion.

There were occasions when that same clerk was trusted with barrister's domestic tasks and errands. A usual one (before the days of mobile telephones) was please, when they went out of chambers to a consultation with leading counsel or to a library, to telephone a wife and tell her that her husband would be home on the late train. Invariably he would fail in this task because nobody had answered the telephone. When asked on counsel's return to chambers if he had given the message to his wife, he would explain the reason why not and with a grin would add his perennial joke, which never ceased to amuse him.

"Always the last to know, Sir."

And he did add the word 'SIR'." That joke could one day backfire and be very unamusing.

35. Recital

Barrister's tendency to be long winded is very great, despite advice from the Romans in antiquity: *Vir sapit qui pauca loquitur* 'it is a wise man who says little'and *paucis verbis* 'with few words'. This springs in part perhaps from that feeling, which often follows lost cases: if only I had said this or that, might it have made a difference?

A judge sitting in the Royal Courts of Justice in the Strand had become weary of the protracted dull case, which had occupied him for several days. Hoping that the tiresome saga might be coming near its end, he adjourned for lunch and inquired of counsel:

"Are we in sight of the end of this matter?"

"My Lord I would hope to finish my speech by the end of today."

"I am so glad to hear that. From the way things have gone already in this case I had feared that after lunch you might read me the psalms from beginning to end."

36. Protraction

In courts, which were situated off what used to be called The Official Referee's Corridor, cases of great weight, length and complexity were tried by specialist judges known as Official Referees (now called The Technology and Construction Courts). These cases, in particular building construction and engineering disputes, tended to be protracted, exacting and exhausting for all concerned. One whose building or motorway was defective might for example sue the builder and/or contractor. They then might blame the constructional engineer, he might blame the architect, he might blame the quantity surveyor and so on. Against the possibility that the allegations made against one or more of these might be made out, it was usually incumbent upon the plaintiff (claimant) to add each one of them as defendants in the action. This made for unwieldy actions with each party represented by separate counsel.

Should the matter come to trial considerable skill was required to avoid too much repetition. On one occasion, in a matter being tried by Judge Newey, some eight counsel were involved. Each got up to cross-examine a witness and to try to extract anything that might assist his particular client. The seventh counsel to take his turn rather lost himself in the labyrinthine detail and began to investigate matters already covered (several times!) by other counsel. Comatose with boredom Judge Newey waited patiently to see whether some small relevant fact might emerge from the morass. It didn't and he intervened at last gently to admonish errant counsel.

"Please, we really must try to avoid repetition."

"Indeed, indeed Your Honour."

37. Geographical expedition

In a county court a young barrister arrived for an application listed for 2 p.m. In the robing room he found only two counsel, evidently opponents engaged in a current contested case. Their respective countenances suggested that they were not getting on too well.

"What are you doing here? . . . . " asked one of the new arrival.

". . . nothing else is listed?"

"I'm in an emergency application, which is being slid in. It should take only five minutes."

"Lucky, young man . . ." came the reply in acid tones, plainly intended for the ear of his opponent.

". . . I think that after lunch, on form to date, it is the intention of my learned friend here to introduce a new topic and to argue endlessly about the sources of the Nile."

Was the complainant perhaps about to lose a lucrative case for the next day?

38. Authorities

It is customary for opposing barristers to exchange lists of authorities in advance of trial; that is for each to apprise the other of the books and cases (with page numbers) to be referred to in support of one party's case and/or against that of the opposition. This practice is obviously sensible and saves a lot of time. It is not however always honoured in spirit. Plainly each party will in this way be given some or a better idea of what may be argued by the other. There will usually be advantage in late delivery (leaving an opponent insufficient time to read and digest the material) and over time this tends to produce a climate of tit for tat. Of course pressure of work will often be responsible: the busy advocate, working all hours may not himself know until the night before exactly what authorities he will need. But there are those who cheat and those who are honourable, and don't. Unfortunately the latter are disadvantaged, not rewarded for their *bona fides* and are tempted to right the balance by like dishonourable behaviour.

One extreme episode is as amusing as it is dreadful. Counsel found themselves opposed in a matter of some complexity. Both delivered lists of their authorities in commendably good time, a week ahead of trial. The list of one identified four authorities, that of the other one hundred and four! Conscientiously the one attacked his daunting reading task in plenty of time: but he became progressively baffled. The day of trial arrived and in the robing room, with diffident courtesy, he raised his difficulty with his opponent.

"Please don't answer me if you feel that it may in any way compromise your case. It's your authorities: the first four listed I can see may have some peripheral bearing. Are you able and willing please to give me some idea as to what line of contention may be supported by all those others? I confess myself unable to find any relevance . . . . . and it is not for want of trying."

A long pause followed as his opponent appeared to consider whether or not to oblige. Then he began to laugh and laugh, long and loud. He was a big man and did much of this with his shoulders: plainly hugely amused.

"I've been killing myself every time I think of you reading all them irrelevant authorities."

39. *Deep in it*

There is a perhaps apocryphal story about Sir Thomas Beecham. When asked if he had ever heard any Stockhausen he is supposed to have replied:

"No, but I believe I have stepped in some."

With only a slight legal nexus is the comparable experience of Queen's Counsel walking to the underground and thence to his chambers on a sunny summer morning along a residential road in Hampsted. He became aware of a sliding sensation and looked down anticipating a banana skin upon which he had stepped. Alas it was something much worse. An enormous squidgy dog turd had almost buried his shoe and already was releasing a positive death cloud of disagreeable smell. Unthinkably awful expletives shot from his mouth in remarkable combination and permutation as he realised what it had done to his lovely new and expensive black Church's brogue shoes and appreciated that a substantial cleaning up operation was necessary if those in the underground were not to be overcome.

His eye fell upon a small gate the other side of which was a stretch of beautifully manicured green lawn. Inside the gate he proceeded to wipe the worst off his cherished new shoe on the grass. The front door burst open as the furious owner ran from the house waving his arms.

"What do you think you are doing?" he shouted.

"Wiping from my pristine shoes the disgusting mess left by your dog just outside your gate on the pavement for pedestrians to step in."

A remarkable presumption, especially from a QC. It cried out for rebuttal, which was comprehensive:

"But I haven't got a dog." he screamed.

40. Language problem

Very young counsel set out one day in the 1960s for the Buckinghamshire Quarter sessions to be held in the quaint mediaeval court at Aylesbury: its dock surrounded by black spiked railings.

His task was to prosecute two Indians, who had allegedly been involved in a serious punch up in an Indian restaurant and who had been indicted for various serious assaults.

The case had been returned to him only the night before by much more senior counsel. He was rather junior to take on such a case. It had had him up for much of the night and he felt distinctly nervous. The main witness, called Patel, did not speak English and did not appear to have a Christian (or forename) to distinguish him from a number of other witnesses of that name. Confusion threatened.

Arrival at court brought unnerving news. The court was to be presided over by Lord Justice Arthian (Beetle) Davies, a demanding no-nonsense man, fierce and notorious for his short fuse and intolerance of any kind of incompetence or inefficiency. The white wig's nightmare. Trouble threatened. Panic threatened. Several of the witnesses did not speak English and, though an interpreter had been provided, it was notoriously more difficult to control the flow of evidence in such circumstances.

The jury was empanelled and counsel opened the case to them, then called the first witness, a Mr Ahmed. He does not remember how he struggled through the oath, affirmation or other of this witness and of the interpreter. Perhaps the clerk of the court assisted or even took over. What he does recollect is that it was all rather traumatic and served to stir up the chairman's ire unhappily early in the proceedings.

Counsel explained that he would ask questions which he, the interpreter, should translate exactly and direct to the witness. The witness should in turn answer and that answer should be exactly translated into English for the court.

Counsel's first question brought forth an apparent argument between the witness and the interpreter, who were clearly not doing as asked. Chairman's unrest began to show. Counsel explained to the interpreter that argumentative conversations were not permitted. Nothing improved and the chairman vented his wrath on counsel who by now could see no end to this case.

Equally he just didn't know what to do or what more might be expected of him. Huge confusion now prevailed and the chairman was in a rage.

"Please try to control this shambles. I have asked you before" he said in warning tones. As he had feared, it did not help that everybody involved seemed to be called Patel. The situation continued to degenerate. The chairman's temper went from bad to worse. In despair counsel pleaded miserably with the interpreter:

"Please, why won't you do what I ask of you?"

"Very sorry but it has to be a very big problem."

"What do you mean? . . ." said the chairman, intervening . . . it is really very simple."

"Oh no. Very difficult, very very difficult you see. I speak Urdu, he speak Punjabi."

41. In a public place

Sooner or later the young common law barrister will probably find himself called upon to defend a flasher. There are quite a few of them about. For the uninitiated it should be known that it is an offence for a male person in a public place lewdly to expose his person with intent to insult a female.

'Flasher' is the informal name given to those who criminally indulge in such behaviour. By repute these gentlemen (men?) wear old and grubby raincoats (known as 'the flasher's mac') the front of which dramatically they draw aside like curtains revealing all, the main item habitually in mode rampant, to a pre-selected lady victim.

Counsel of only a few years standing opened a brief to discover that the lot had fallen upon him at last: he had to defend an alleged flasher: but one who had not been wearing a mac; one who was *prima facie* a respectable professional man in middle age. A bandage, following surgery, had discomfited him acutely and, despite the public place, he had found it necessary to attend to it urgently, and that had involved adjusting his clothing. Despite the hurry he had been most discreet and nobody could have seen anything, which they should not have done. A thumb might have been momentarily visible. Heavens alive there was certainly no intenton to insult anybody. Frankly he had not noticed any woman or indeed anyone at all who might have imagined herself to be insulted.

Counsel trudged out to the magistrates court in outer London. It was very crowded and the case was called on before he had had much time to consult with his client. The prosecution described this most disagreeable and unacceptable episode and called the witness to it. How could the accused not have noticed her? A stunningly pretty young woman entered the witness box: slender, beautifully groomed with long blond hair and wearing a tight fitting pale blue tweed suit.

She described her horrid experience ably assisted by the chairman of the bench, who seemed to presume guilt and couldn't wait to pronounce such a verdict, with those rebuffing words, "we find the case proved." But, cross examined, she accepted that it had been dusk, that she was some 15 yards away, that she was distracted by a taxi she hoped to catch and, above all, that her determining piece of evidence was merely a glance because, as she readily agreed with counsel who, by way of question, declared himself sure that she would not let her eye dwell for very long upon something like that which she had purported to see. The gravamen of what was being said was that no nice young woman would permit her gaze to rest upon such a thing for long and counsel did rather dwell upon this in varying permutation before putting his case, so that she began to appear as an awful woman if she continued to profess to have seen what the prosecution alleged. "You could have seen a thumb, which I suggest was the fact?" "I don't think that it was, but it might have been." Enough for an undeniable reasonable doubt. That it took the magistrates nearly an hour to return and announce 'case dismissed' was astonishing.

The client was being effusively grateful, as they jostled in a still crowded hallway outside, when counsel noticed the erstwhile lady complainant determinedly fighting her way obviously towards him through the throng. Wow! he thought, mind now off the case, she really was devastating. He filled with pleased anticipation but couldn't imagine what she might have to say to him. His heart missed a beat, then beat ever faster as she came closer and closer. Then she arrived and looked him straight and ferociously in the eye, before bursting into tears as she pummelled his chest with her fist, sobbing and declaring "I'll hate you 'til I die."

Very sad.

42. Balls

Balls. The word has a certain fascination as meaning, amongst other things, boldness and rubbish but always with its association with male equipment giving it a certain humorous quality, reflecting perhaps long past schoolboy mirth never wholly shaken off; amusement at such things as playing pocket billiards. Traces have filtered into the law where its influence can be seen to persist. So in an alleged tampering with the seam of cricket balls case involving Pakistan, a number of balls with seams in varying state of mutilation were handed to witnesses giving evidence in the witness box. When cross-examination had finished the judge's grin, scarcely concealed, was the 'give-away' of schoolboy influence as he asked if Mr Carman might have his balls back.

One barrister used the word so often that there was temptation to keep a tally of how often he used it to rubbish opponent's points in a given case. He caught them out once by reaching his final speech to a jury without mention of it. But then he began his address: "Members of the jury, the prosecution has bowled an awful lot of balls at you in this case. Let me demonstrate why . . ."

In another case a rogue accused of stealing some valuable gold and platinum rings had allegedly thrown them away in the owner's garden when detection threatened. This he denied stoutly. The owner, he contended must just have lost them. It was not a promising defence but that is not unusual. The number and the spread in a long-grassed area, in which they were found and recovered, were put to him by counsel so as to demonstrate the inherent unlikelihood of what he maintained when he fought back in protest: "you keep on going on about losing things being not likely, but its gospel truth. Me, I keep on losing things all the time. Reckon I'd lose me balls if I didn't have a bag to keep 'em in."

43. Which county?

His Honour Judge Claude Duveen sat in the courts of Buckinghamshire. He sat one day in a county court in that county. Before him counsel battled out the apportionment of responsibility for the damage caused in a motor collision and now the subject of dispute in what is known in the profession as a 'running down' case, 'runner' for short. This was very dull stuff and his Honour was hard put to stave off sleep. At last he intervened:

"What is all this time wasting argument about? What county are we in?"

Both counsel were surprised and bewildered but each was pleased to name the same and the correct county.

The judge seemed satisfied with an answer to only the second question and the case dragged on: but a little later he intervened again.

"I thought you both knew what county we are in but it seems

that I must ask again lest more time be wasted in superfluous argument. What county are we in?"

Both counsel answered dutifully with the name of the same and the correct county, wondering if senility had taken a hold.

"Did you both not know that in that county all apportionments of damage are fifty-fifty? It does save such a lot of time."

Circa 1972, in another county, Lincolnshire, a young barrister learned an interesting fact. He had come up from London to contest a damage only motor collision case. Two cars travelling on a straight road had collided head on. Each could be shown to have been about nine inches over the centre of the road, there seemed to be no question of a last minute movement by either driver and there was good visibility of about a mile in both directions. It seemed to be an obvious case of fifty-fifty but neither party would accept any responsibility. The solicitor met counsel at the station and they chatted as they drove to court.

"I'm at a loss to understand the protagonist's attitude in this case," said the barrister.

"Well you see . . ." answered the solicitor " . . . despite the good straight roads, the flat open fertile country and the sparse population, we have the greatest number of accidents *per capita* in the country. They are all farmers and, as they study, assess and compare with their own the crops of others, they drive endlessly into everybody and everything and never seem to reckon that it is their fault."

44. Philanthropist

A witness involved in a motor accident once made a statement to the police concerning what had happened. It is perhaps self-interested and speaks for itself: an extract read as follows:

"I was driving my brand new MG car (I'd had it for only a week) along the road in question towards a roundabout into which four roads led. I could see over the central reservation and noticed a motor cyclist coming towards me in the road immediately opposite. At that moment I also saw a blue car coming towards the roundabout from the road to my right. I slowed to give way to the blue car and was coming quite close to the entrance to the roundabout. The motorcyclist seemed to be going very fast and did not slow down as he approached. Whether he didn't see the blue car or whether he assumed that it would give way to him, I don't know. The blue car did not give way and, as it entered the roundabout, moved into the path of the motorcyclist, who swerved to avoid collision. He did not succeed and hit the front of the car. There was a terrific bang as the motorcycle fell over and skidded away. The rider flew up into the air and, after landing, slid at great speed along the road surface towards me before his crash-helmeted head came into violent collision with the front of my car. He did a terrible lot of damage to my new car!"

Nothing was said about the head of the poor motor cyclist!

Doubtless in due course the driver of the blue car would assert that classic hopeless excuse advanced by so many who have failed to keep a proper lookout; "I never saw the motor cyclist. He must have been going very fast." He was indeed but he was not invisible.

45. Trespassers

A decision of the Divisional Court in 1982 may be of interest to all drinking drivers. Police followed a car, the driver of which they suspected of having consumed alcohol.

When he arrived home, the driver got out of his car and went to enter his house. The officers followed him entering onto his land where they intended to ask him please to take a breathaliser test. He pre-empted them by inviting them to 'fuck off'. They did not respond to this firm if vernacular directive and did not and would not leave the premises. He declined to take a breathaliser test for which, in due course, he was prosecuted.

The driver contended that the police officers had no entitlement to ask him to take a breathaliser test because they had no right to be on his premises, their *prima facie* implied licence having been revoked by use of the very forceful words substituted for 'go away'. They had become trespassers. The court held that these words were mere vulgar abuse and did not operate so as to revoke the licence and leave them as trespassers.

One has to wonder what form of words might have sufficed to revoke the implied licence. A stronger directive can scarcely be imagined, even if simple and less offensive ones can. This will have to be left to more powerful legal intellects in higher courts. Perhaps it may be very simple: a small more specific addition may serve to revoke the licence: 'f . . k off *out of my garden*': more specific than vulgar abuse *simpliciter*. See Snook v Mannion [1962] Crim L.R. 601

46. Surprise

The running down case goes a long way to provide the staple diet of common law barristers at all stages of their careers. Vehicles continue to collide and be damaged: drivers and their passengers continue to get injured. Who is liable? How, if at all, is fault causative of any ensuing injury or damage to be apportioned and what sum of money is appropriate for compensatory damages are the perpetual areas where dispute may arise. When dispute does emerge, the outcome is seldom obvious or predictable, so numerous are the varying combinations of fact and circumstance which may have a bearing.

A warning example lies in the experience of a young common lawyer who received instructions to contest liability for a serious cross roads collision. He was well instructed; the police report was full with sketches of all positions of witnesses and of any unsighting obstacles including a canvas electrician's hut. For the defendant driver he found one witness particularly adverse but as he measured the hut and assiduously drew sight lines from where this key witness was shown to be, he convinced himself that the witness could not have seen that which he maintained that he had. He arrived at court bursting with optimism, reckoning that in cross-examination he could destroy this witness and win the case. In due course the time came for his cross examination. He handed his sketch plan to the witness.

"You were standing where a cross is shown on the plan?"

"Yes."

"Behind a black canvas electricity hut-like structure, for want of a better description?"

"Yes."

"Sight lines are drawn on the plan, do you see them?"

"Yes."

"They show the possible vision from behind the canvas erection where you were?"

"Yes."

"Is it not quite clear that you could not have seen this collision?

"No."

"You surmised afterwards what you thought must have happened?"

"I didn't."

"You mean you say that you could see?"

"Yeah I had a grandstand view."

There was silence for a few moments.

"You see I was where you asked me on the plan and I agree all the other things you said but, you see, I was standing, resting and looking around with my head about nine inches above the ground: in a hole I'd just dug."

This is the unexpected torpedo, called litigation hazard.

47. Clean shoes

Commuting to the Temple means for some barristers early rising. One such traveller, who lived in the country, was always up and gone to catch his train long before his children got up to go to school, let alone wakened. In the fullness of time dad was made a Recorder: bottom of the pile part-time judiciary. First step on the *cursus honorum* 'route to high public office.' It was a mixed blessing. He was not a criminal lawyer and, in his short part time visits to the Crown Courts, he found stressful the abiding fear that he would perpetrate some humiliating fundamental error, which would make him look like the idiot he felt. Against that the Court was not far from his home and he could get up considerably later and eat breakfast with his wife and children. On one such occasion an eleven year old daughter saw him cleaning his shoes before he left, something he did every morning, conditioned by the most draconian punishment meted out in school days for presenting with dirty shoes: but she had not before been up early enough to witness this daily ritual.

"Are you cleaning your shoes Dad, because the judge will be cross if they are dirty?"

"Today, Theresa, it just so happens that I am the judge."

Disbelief was manifest. Dad had a funny sense of humour and was clearly joking. A prophet indeed is not without honour, save in his own country, and in his own house. St. Matthew 13:57. But at court, for the coming two weeks, he would be addressed as 'Your Honour.'

48. Work Experience

Circa 1998 a young man (a schoolboy still) found himself filled with joie de vivre one spring morning. A friendly world seemed to beckon. He had just been accepted to read law amongst the dreaming spires and the careers master at school had arranged for him to spend a week in London barristers' chambers, to see the every day workings of that part of the legal profession. This was called work experience. He rather fancied the idea of wearing a wig. And a week off school! He imagined the excitement of grisly murder cases, outrageous libels and vehement forensic contests in the courts.

On arrival the clerk greeted him and led him to the room of a young successful barrister in whose charge he was left.

"I do apologise, I have to leave you for the morning. But no harm done, do you good to look at some papers and see how work looks when it comes….."

He pointed to a side table on which was piled a daunting heap of red taped bundles of papers.

"Take any one or more of these, read it, think about what the solicitor asks be done, advise, settle pleadings etc. Here try this one, it's new in this morning . . . ."

He handed over a set.

"You can tell me about it over lunch and I'll organise the rest of your week. Good luck."

With that he vanished. The young man sat down and looked at what he had been handed. 'Mr Vernon Trenchard, instructions to counsel to advise on behalf of proposed plaintiff' it said on the front. 'What is a plaintiff?' he wondered as enthusiastically he removed the red ribbon. A large Oxford Dictionary was to hand, but he did not get so far as using it; his attention was distracted as the picture of a very very pretty girl appeared under the backsheet.

She warranted some moments of careful study and admiration before he discovered in a bundle of photographs the picture of an unusually good looking young man followed by a series showing variously a staircase, a close-up of the polished walnut handrail on a banister, the room at the top of it and that at the bottom.

The litigation proposed was pursued by the actor's union Equity and the young man and woman had been acting out a part in a scene from a riotous party being filmed. The last photo showed the same man evidently in hospital with much of his body covered in plaster of paris. It appeared that he wished to claim damages for negligence in respect of injuries against the director and makers of the film.

The photographs showed all. At this hilarious party it had been intended that the lovely girl should slide down the banister to be gathered up and twirled round in the arms of the dashing drop dead gorgeous young man. Alas, nothing so romantic. As she descended she gathered great speed and unanticipated momentum. The young man bravely caught her but was overwhelmed and hurled to the polished parquet floor. His body cushioned her but he broke an awful lot of bones.

Mr Trenchard returned unexpectedly soon.

"Well young man, learned some law this morning? Come, we'll go out for coffee."

He didn't need to answer as briskly they made off. He was seized of no forensic learning. All that passed through his schoolboy mind was: 'how disastrously sad that such a lovely girl should fall into your arms in such a way as to land you sore wounded in hospital. And he still didn't know what a plaintiff was.

49. Explosive

The adversarial system of the English courts can lead to heated exchange and make it hard work to maintain the traditional form of mutual courteous address, 'my learned friend.' Sometimes a happy (unhappy?) surprise can intervene, as it were, to break the ice.

Two seasoned practitioners, engaged in the Crown Court, had slugged it out for several days. Evading tax was the crime alleged: very serious. Time for speeches to the jury arrived at last. Prosecuting counsel was a heavyweight in every sense of the word. Big, smooth and fast talking in his booming voice, his final speech to the jury made every conceivable point before urging that only a verdict of guilty would do. His opponent was more than his equal as an advocate and tactician: he sat, poised, ready to answer and to leap instantly up the moment the prosecution sat down: so as to follow with like momentum and energy on behalf of the accused. The prosecution's address hurtled on until suddenly he urged, yet again and finally, a verdict of 'guilty'. As he sat dramatically and heavily down an immediate thunderous explosion resounded through the court and seemed to rock the building to its very foundations. Nobody doubted what it was. Defence counsel, moving already to his feet, sat instantly down again:

"Oh dear!" he exclaimed. "So sorry. I thought that my learned friend had finished his final address."

Nobody (save prosecuting counsel) seemed upset. Courtroom decorum was not entirely maintained.

50. Tact

Pupils are there to learn the practical ropes from an older barrister of experience, a pupil master or mistress. To see at first hand in practice so much of what is not to be found in law books on the basis of the ancient Roman adage *a bove majori discit arare minor* 'a young ox learns to plough from an older one.'

Sometimes active teaching rather than passive absorption is needed.

Half way through his twelve month pupillage a young barrister received his first instructions to advise in writing. The joy and thrill were quickly superseded by irritation. Vital documents and correspondence were missing. It was quite impossible to deal with the matter in its current state. He telephoned the solicitor from his pupil master's room, made his complaint directly in tones of critical irritation, spelling out (as a great favour and with a certain unconscious arrogance) exactly what was needed still. Once finished he felt better. He had put that useless fellow in his place.

"I couldn't help overhearing your conversation" said his pupil master raising his head. "Just remember that solicitors are going to be your bread and butter. If you need to criticise them, wrap it up, soften the blow with gentle courtesy and excuses for him or her . . . I'm sure you've been terribly busy etc., etc. Don't worry about whether it's unfounded; diplomatic flattery is the order of the day. It's probably one of his smallest and least important cases not meriting much of his time. From what I heard I doubt that you will ever see that fellow again. Fledgling barristers should refrain from kicking the arses of solicitors with one foot before they are quite confident that they can stand on the other leg."

He never did see that fellow again.

Pupils for their part should be industrious and courteously deferential, seen but non-interfering and not unnecessarily heard. Very seldom are all these attributes found in one who is also supportive, able, amusing and clever. One most important gift a pupil may have is the ability to see and get on with what needs to be done without bothering his busy and harassed master.

One pupil is remembered for behaviour which nearly over-stepped the mark. At a conference of his master he sat deferentially at the back of the room, having been identified and introduced. The matter was somewhat of an emergency and there had been very little to read from which to learn what it was all about. The solicitor, with the client sitting beside him, undertook to do the job verbally. He set to with a long diatribe. Presently the client interrupted to ask if he might 'say a thing'. Of course, he was told and added his bit.

Afterwards the pupil intimated that he had been sore tempted to interrupt the conference.

"Why? Do you think I got the wrong end of the stick?"

"Oh no. Just the practicalities. When the client interrupted to ask if he might say a thing I wanted to leap up and say: "of course you may, you're paying for the whole bloody show!"

"I'm glad you didn't."

51. Candour

The learning curve of the fledgling advocate is formulated by a series of lucky breaks as much as by any organised education. One such barrister, robed and ready to go, was informed by the clerk of the lists that his case, listed for 10.30 a.m., would not come on until midday. He chose to sit and listen to the case underway in the adjoining court. There he found Mr Jeremy Black defending. What luck. Here was a man of whom he had heard his former pupil master speak in tones of reverential awe: one from whom he could learn. A high flyer, a future Lord Chief Justice or Lord Chancellor.

Skill and ability seemed just to ooze out of his commanding tall, slim figure and calm demeanour. His lovely voice and seemingly computerised clear diction were mesmerising. If a witness's honesty was to be impugned, it was not put rudely and challengingly to him that he told a pack of lies. Rather it was suggested to him, with a disarming and compelling charm, which it seemed could admit only of an affirmative answer, that "what you have told this court (naughty boy!) is all absolutely untrue". He seemed incapable of descending to the disagreeable.

The morning provided wonderful surprise instruction in how to handle opposing witnesses. But the highlight was yet to come. A legal technicality arose. The jury left and prosecuting counsel, Mr White, addressed the judge at length.

"Yes, yes", mumbled the judge when eventually he had finished

"What do you have to say about this Mr Black?"

Black rose to his feet. A lucid, succinct, authoritative analysis and answer was expected.

"I fear that I have very little to say. It may be that I am obtuse but I have to confess that I do not understand what is being said."

"I am so glad to hear you say that Mr Black, because neither did I."

He turned to Mr White.

"Mr White, for the benefit of Mr Black and myself, would you please repeat your submission, starting from scratch and taking it very slowly."

Moral. Come clean quickly however stupid you feel that you may appear. Never allow yourself to become bogged down in an ever deepening bottomless muddy pit of non-comprehension.

52. Loot

At the Buckinghamshire Assizes held at Aylesbury circa 1960 a pupil watched admiringly as his pupil master took apart and systematically destroyed the prosecution case against three rough looking alleged robbers sitting in the old black spike surrounded dock. If the indictment was a true bill, they had made off with rather a lot of cash.

Acquittal did not take the jury long after hearing defence counsel's speech, despite the gentle and subtle efforts of the judge in his summing up to retrieve something from the wreckage of the prosecution case. The prisoners were discharged, left the dock, thanked their counsel profusely and joined a couple of ropy looking characters who had been seen to follow the trial from the public gallery.

"Disgraceful that they should have got off" . . . lamented the pupil master as he removed and packed his robes ". . . but my job is to do the best I can for my clients, who are entitled to be defended and I must say the prosecution could have put their case together with greater care."

The lawyer's exit was by a back door. No sooner had they got out on their way to the car park than three men swooped on the pupil master apparently from nowhere. They seemed to manhandle him and the pupil, a sturdy number eight forward on the rugby field, prepared to weigh in on his behalf but heard the words "you was really wonderful, guv, this is to show our appreciation." They were the erstwhile defendants, who vanished as quickly as they had appeared. In his coat pocket the master found two rolls of. banknotes He counted them shortly after, in the car, £750.

"Honour among thieves," he muttered "very generous . . . I mean 'thieves' despite their acquittal: they all have terrible criminal records. I suppose my clerk will want his percentage? I haven't had such a problem before. I won't tell him and don't you dare mention it. I can't keep it of course; I'm on legal aid. I'm going to wrap it up and send it to The Barristers Benevolent Fund . . . . anonymously!"

53. More Pupillage

In the early 1960s a barrister's pupillage was (and largely still is) in the nature of apprenticeship to an experienced senior junior (i.e., not a Queen's Counsel, who no longer take pupils) but the privilege had then to be paid for. The fee was a hundred guineas: a very substantial sum in those days. The pupil learned by a kind of osmosis: he absorbed by reading his master's papers and comparing his own written opinions with those later produced by his master. Sometimes there was discussion. He was of course also privy to his master's briefs to attend court and in a position therefore to compare (and it is to be hoped learn from) the manner in which his master approached the case with how he might himself have done.

In other respects the position had something in common with the officer's batman in the army. A pupil might expect to run errands, which had nothing to do with learning the law but which convenienced the master: buying cigarettes, cheroots or Murraymints, an evening newspaper or (greatly appreciated, for they were always shared) doughnuts and custard tarts for tea.

One event is well remembered. In the fullness of time both pupil and master involved rose to the High Court Bench. The master was owner of a Jack Russell terrier named Smollet. When his wife was likely to be out for most of the day, it was his habit to bring the dog to chambers. He was a very well behaved little fellow, who slept peacefully at his master's feet under the latter's large pedestal desk. There was little or no conversation. A work automaton, the master seldom raised his head from his papers. His pupil sat at a suitably small desk facing a white wall.

One day, when the dog was there, the pupil left the room to collect some law reports. He returned with several volumes and left the door ajar while he put them on his desk before returning to close it. "Shut the door." said the master's fierce imperative directive as he was just about to do so, then did forthwith. "Not you" said the fierce voice, sounding irritable now and all but adding the word 'idiot'. "Open it again." The pupil hastily obliged and noticed that the little dog had emerged from his deep slumber and stood alert with pricked up ears by both their masters' desk. "Shut the door" repeated his master's voice. The little fellow took off and bounded purposefully at speed across the room and with both front paws hurled himself, crash, against the open door. It banged firmly closed.

"That's better" said the master, returning his attention to his work.

54. Monosyllabic

In Gulliver's Travels Jonathan Swift made plain his view of lawyers: ". . . a society of men bred up from their youth in the art of proving by words multiplied for the purpose, that black is white and white is black, according as they are paid".

An idealistic young man, whose ambition from early youth had been to become a barrister, was stung by these words and resolved that they should never include him.

In due course he became a very busy successful barrister. One day a set of papers caused him to fly into a rage. He telephoned the instructing solicitor and gave free reign.

"I am returning these papers. No thought has been given to the issues. In consequence so many documents are missing that I am quite unable to deal with the matter. Please inform the insurance claims manager of the reasons for delay. This has wasted a great deal of my time when I am working under pressure. I have listed information and documents needed." Uncomplimentary mono-syllabic comment, variously critical, patronising, superior and rude was additionally made in response to feeble would be exculpatory protest.

Oh dear! he thought as he calmed down after putting back the phone. The insurers are very good clients of chambers and I should know better at my age.

Within a few minutes the phone rang.

"The insurance claims manager in that case you've just sent back wants to speak to you Sir." said his clerk. "He's been speaking to the solicitor."

"Oh dear!"

The ensuing conversation did not take long.

"I'm told that you can't give expedition to my electrocution case."

"Right."

"Why?"

"Ill prepared. Too much missing."

"There is complaint from my solicitor that you were variously critical, patronising, superior and rude. Were you critical?"

"Yes."

Pause.

"Were you patronising?"

"I suppose so."

"Were you superior?"

"Yes. Annoyed."

"Were you rude?"

"Yes. Sorry."

"Thank you. All I needed to know."

The phone rang again five minutes later. It was his clerk.

"The claims manager you were just talking to Sir has just been on to me. He's very impressed by your direct approach. Very straightforward economy of language. No waffle or beating around the bush. He's fed up with long winded barristers and proposes to direct many more of his heaviest cases to you. Well done Sir."

Gracious, he thought. Perhaps there is something in G.K. Chesterton's 'he that expecteth nothing shall be gloriously rewarded.'

55. Driving a car

Penury is a great bugbear during pupillage. Income is non-existent, negligible if you are lucky. Mr Pickwick had been rightly told: 'what fine places of slow torture barristers' chambers are: the waiting — the hope – the disappointment – the fear – the misery – the poverty.' Things had not changed that much. This was the immediate prospect for one while still a pupil and running up debt.

Travel posed a real problem, particularly for those operating on the circuits. It cost so much, yet experience of courtroom practice and etiquette was top of the priority list. A sometime pupil told of his experiences.

"My pupil master was the kindest and most likeable of men. When he went on circuit he invited me to stay in his home: a great treat for he had a pretty and charming wife and two lovely daughters. And he arranged to pick me up and drove me endlessly to court with him. The trouble was that he was a terrible driver and, like so many such drivers, was quite unaware of the fact and that regularly he scared the very daylights out of me.

He would regale me with anecdotes and lawyers' tales as we drove along. On one occasion his driving was particularly bad. My seatbelt tightened as I slipped as far as I could back into my seat, beads of cold perspiration glistening on my forehead. He hurtled up to every car in front, then braked furiously again and again and at traffic lights I wondered if he might be colour blind. He chatted the while.

"My dear old father . . ." he told me ". . . was a terrible driver. As he grew older his eyesight seriously impaired his already questionable competence. I remember being driven by him near Windsor. It was shortly after the end of the war, before demob. There were soldiers in uniform everywhere. We were going to a lunch at which all manner of VIPs were to attend. Suddenly we came upon a large flock of sheep blocking the carriageway. They progressed unbearably slowly along in front of us. My father was one for punctuality and I fully expected an outburst of irritation. Yet he remained remarkably composed and tolerant of the delay and inconvenience they occasioned. There was no sign of the short fuse ordinarily to be expected as we crawled along and became already late for our appointment. Then all was revealed: 'fine body of fighting men. I'm full of admiration.'"

56. Delirium tremens

Barristers must take care not to drink too much when they might be up-front next day. Most are familiar with the dire symptoms of hangover: more debilitating and more awful than many serious diseases, yet attracting no sympathy for the utter misery endured.

A young and ordinarily very responsible young barrister was on the verge of breaking into the big time with 'big boy' solicitors coming to see him in conference on a very heavy matter next day. That evening an old colleague turned up at his bachelor flat. "I'm leaving London, going to Bristol chambers. Come, I'll buy you dinner at the French bistro, The Bistingo, in Fleet Street." Before departing the flat they emptied a bottle of Beaujolais and with dinner finished more than one large carafe of house wine. In a pub after, there was only room for shorts, scotch to be exact, several of them. It was a good evening.

He had no memory of going to bed. Next morning he awoke at seven o'clock and lay for a little. I feel OK he thought as he remembered that conference, potentially vital to his immediate career. Then he noticed his clothes strewn all over the floor. "I don't remember doing that" he thought and realised that he was not wearing any pyjamas. They remained folded under his pillow. At least he was under the blankets, not suffering hypothermia. Wow, I must have been far gone. Never known anything like this before. But I don't feel bad. What a man I must be. He moved then for the first time from the horizontal to the vertical position intending to get up. My God, he thought, I'm not a man after all as a wave of potent nausea overwhelmed him and set off an involuntary heaving, which went on and on without relieving result. He reverted to the horizontal position so as to restore himself and found that he had broken out in a cold sweat.

In that position he felt not too bad but could move to no other without inducing onset of acute symptoms of nauseous illness. By crawling he made the bathroom and thought that drinking a little water would help: but no, it set off the most violent heaving reaction. This was becoming serious. It was now ten o'clock and his conference was at eleven fifteen. Feeling really terrible, he struggled into his clothes and made his way unsteadily to chambers: it was only a short walk. He avoided his clerk and sat down at his desk with the absurdly unrealistic hope that these waves of sickening nausea would abate in the five minutes recovery time left to him.

The conference deputation seemed to arrive immediately. The solicitor showed a certain hostile arrogance; not yet sure of this young man previously untried. They launched straight in. The sickly mind was showered with documents. The print jumped up and down and made no impact on his brain. Then, as that awful heaving began again to well up inside and he felt the sweat build up in beads on his forehead, he thought, "my God, I just can't throw up right here."

Until now nobody had appeared to notice his distress: he had been careful not to speak more than was absolutely necessary. But now the chips were down.

"I'm afraid you will have to excuse me for a moment" he blurted suddenly out as he stood up and rushed from the room. In the loo he endured spasmodic uncontrollable heaving and became drenched in sweat. He knew he couldn't go on and, after more than a few moments, returned to the assembled company.

"I am terribly sorry to tell you that you will have to come on another day. You see I feel simply terrible. I think I must have eaten something last night."

The euphemism or white (black?) lie inherent in those last words (though misleading, true in substance and in fact) were not lost on the solicitor whose look of fury said all. He knew the form. Irresponsible young puppy: wasting his time (charged at £300 an hour then? What now, 20 years on?!) They departed and never did come back.

The moral is clear.

57. Returns

The returned brief is a fearful thing. It comes about in various ways but more often than not results when counsel is involved in a case, which goes on for longer than anticipated, so that suddenly it clashes with another trial listed unexpectedly by the court officers: or already booked for him, often for hearing on the very next day.

The brief for that case is returned to another frequently not too pleased barrister, usually at around five thirty. It interrupts his out of court advisory written work schedule: the short notice often has him up for most of the night in preparation; he does not agree with the original counsel's optimistic assessment of the prospects, he is unhappy with the way it has been pleaded: the advice on evidence has, in his view, much to be desired (who is to come to court to prove what, what documents have been agreed . . . ?) and so on and so forth. But there is on record the ultimate potential disaster to which counsel should be alert. It is narrated here in the first person by one who experienced it.

It was 5.45 on a Thursday evening. The week had been hectic and stressful, littered with injunctions and other emergencies. I was deep into a complicated opinion, which had languished too long in the 'too difficult' pile and for which the solicitors were screaming. It was scheduled (so far as that is ever possible to achieve in the law) for completion the next day and I looked forward unusually to a work free weekend and the relaxation of cutting my grass. "Come in" I said irritably in answer to a knock on my door. I really didn't need to be disturbed. It was Ernest my clerk.

"Sir, brace yourself for some bad news. Mr Jones has gone part heard in Nottingham and has this case fixed for tomorrow over the road in the RCJ (Royal Courts of Justice). You are the only person available to take it on. I know you are under pressure Sir but I have no alternative but to ask you. You don't know the solicitors but I have spoken to them and they would be most grateful to you if you would take it on. Patrick Smith is the name of the solicitor dealing with it."

He was not asking me, he was directing me and had set it all up and pushed me into a corner. I was to be a good public/chambers spirited boy and do as I was told. Protest was pointless but musn't be too compliant, be seen as a soft touch and taken advantage of. Protest I did, though I knew it was as to fart against thunder: to no avail.

"It's in your line of expertise, Sir. Shouldn't be too trouble-some."

"O.K." I said at last with the greatest of reluctance. He hadn't shown me the papers. They were one foot high A4!

The case turned out to be a nightmare. Full of complication it had me up virtually all night, kept awake by a torrential flow of adrenalin hurtling through my veins and increasing to tsunami proportions as I encountered one, as it seemed to me, insuperable difficulty after another. The pleadings were inade-quate and, despite my short acquaintance with it, I rated the case a complete loser on every score. How it had ever been allowed to get as far as court I could not imagine.

By the time I crossed that Zebra crossing in front of the Royal Courts of Justice in the Strand, I was in a lather of nervous apprehension. Robed up I arrived early at the appointed court. I looked for suitable candidates for solicitor in my case, Onus v Burden, and called for Mr Smith. Response came at last as I began to despair.

"You are Patrick Smith solicitor in Onus v Burden?"

He nodded. I introduced myself and immediately launched into a nervous unstoppable verbal torrent, explaining my deep pessimism for our prospects: anxious to impart my views and get the whole ghastly business off my chest as soon as possible. It just spilled out of me, giving him no chance to respond. I concluded:

"I'm sorry to have to tell you that I rate our chances in this case at nil, it is utterly hopeless and there is no money in court so, whatever sum we can manage to screw the plaintiff down to, we will have no answer to paying all their costs, probably on an indemnity basis."

"Please, no more. I have to interrupt you. You give me no opportunity to speak. You see, I am indeed Patrick Smith, solic-itor in Onus v Burden but I have to tell you that I am solicitor for the plaintiff (claimant)!"

58. Collisions

There is a story, apocryphal perhaps, about Lord Lane when he was Lord Chief Justice. It is said that, travelling home one evening, his car came into collision with a lorry in the Strand. It was not a very serious matter but enough damage was done for it to be likely that, as is usually the case, the amazing apparently disproportionate cost of repair would cause outrage. Both drivers left their vehicles and His Lordship was surprised to hear the suggestion that it had been all his fault.

"If that is your view" said the judge "we had better go by the book. Perhaps you would let me have your name and address, the name of your employer, the index number of your vehicle, your insurer's name and please tell me anything you would like to say about the accident itself."

"By the bleedin book, Mr high and mighty. S'pose you think you're the Lord Chief bleedin Justice?"

"Well it just so happens that I am."

There is another story, equally apocryphal perhaps, concerning the same judge. Driving on a motorway he was involved in a minor collision with a white van. It was however sufficient to cause both drivers to draw up and stop on the hard shoulder to deal with all necessary requirements of the law. Familiar with the reputation, deserved or not, of the 'white van man', His Lordship felt it not only fair but prudent to show his hand.

"Before we embark upon any discussion of this incident and deal with what the law requires of us, I think I should tell you that I am the Lord Chief Justice."

"Oh Gawd, just my f . . . ing luck."

59. Unanimous verdict!

In the days when the verdict of juries had to be unanimous, barristers were subjected to much suffering and inconvenience. So that vast sums of taxpayer's money were not wasted (as disagreement usually involved the cost of a re-trial) juries were sent out whenever possible early in the day. In this way, as time passed, there was ample scope for judicial assistance and greater potential for avoidance of ultimate disagreement.

Judges would call the jury out after they had deliberated for a reasonable time and ask whether there was any prospect of their reaching a verdict which was unanimous: he would remind them of any law causing them difficulty, answer for them any questions he could, remind them from his note of any evidence they asked about and frequently permit them to take for close scrutiny any item exhibited during the trial.

Invariably he sent them back to continue in their attempts to reach a verdict which was unanimous, one on which they were all agreed. The passage of time itself brought pressure to bear.

One such case survives in memory. On a hot and humid summers day a jury at the famous London Sessions deliberated interminably. The accused was said to have raided a shop and stolen, amongst other things, a wad of a thousand used £5 notes, a lot of money in those days. At nearly five o'clock all concerned outside the jury room (and probably some within), had become bored out of their minds with the waiting. They had been first sent out at ten forty five. A weary and disconsolate looking judge summoned them to his presence, not for the first time that day.

"Is there any reasonable prospect that you may yet reach a verdict which is unanimous?" he asked.

The foreman nodded unconvincingly. Others just looked glum and one shook his head.

"Can I help in any way?" asked the judge "... for it means great expense to the exchequer if you cannot reach a verdict and a retrial may have to be ordered."

"It might just help" said the foreman "if we could have exhibit twelve (the bundle of one thousand used five pound notes) in the jury room so that we might give it closer scrutiny." What they could discern from any, let alone closer, scrutiny was not obvious but a tired judge was not disposed to quibble; he was ready to order anything if it might help to bring forth a verdict and let all concerned go home. He asked them yet again to retire and attempt to reach a unanimous verdict.

A short time elapsed. The court convened. The foreman of the jury astonishingly announced a verdict of not guilty. The prisoner was discharged, the jury thanked for their great patience and perseverance and judge, counsel, jury and court staff all hurried off home at last. The bundle of £5 notes was not found as expected in the jury room and was never seen again!

With the majority verdicts permissible in prescribed circumstances today there may still be long waits for those outside the jury room but they are not now nearly so frequent.

60. Beyond a reasonable doubt

In a criminal prosecution it is for the Crown (the prosecution) to prove guilt. This is called the burden of proof. An accused is presumed innocent until proved guilty by all the evidence adduced in the case, not just that by the prosecution. That proof must be sufficient to leave the jury with no reasonable doubt as to, or so that they feel sure of, the accused's guilt before they should convict. This is called the standard of proof.

What however constitutes feeling sure? How do we recognise that degree of conscious feeling? Discussion of this concept is discouraged, since it is calculated to cause sterile argument and confusion. One barrister took the view that some real and practical example was essential, that abstract concept alone was not satisfactory. When addressing juries he would ask the rhetorical question: what is the meaning of beyond a reasonable doubt or feeling sure? He would then answer: it is the kind of sureness that you would wish to feel about an important decision in your own every day life: when buying a new house in times of economic instability: throwing in a secure job when uncertainty surrounds the prospects of getting a new one: making a proposal of marriage . . . The last mentioned brought interruption from the judge.

"Putting it too high!"

He was a bachelor. But he did later marry.

61. De bene esse

De bene esse is a Latin expression much used by lawyers. Very few have attempted translation (surprisingly) but, even had they done so, they would not satisfactorily have succeeded. Its origin is a mystery. Probably Cicero would have made little sense of this expression, even though made up of words from his own language. Here is not the place for a treatise (for a little more see *Lawyers' Latin new edition* by John Gray). However, by a kind of professional osmosis, the meaning attributed and adopted by the majority of lawyers who use the expression is: 'For what it is worth' or 'For purposes of argument': often coming to much the same thing.

The expression however was used, so a possibly apocryphal story goes, when Lord Lane was chairman of Quarter Sessions, well before he became Lord Chief Justice. Counsel handed up a document supported by the contention that it was *de bene esse*.

"What exactly do those Latin words mean?" asked the chairman (wickedly?). Counsel was momentarily speechless. Then, true to his profession, he found much to say. When eventually he had finished the chairman responded.

"Thank you. I hear what you have to say. What a wonderful language Latin must be. All that in three words."

62. Serving sentence

In the criminal courts there appear quite regularly those jokers who would make light of their predicament in a manner verging on contempt. In one such case a judge had had to threaten to have the accused taken from the court if his smart Alec interruptions did not cease. He was convicted by the jury but kept up his brand of humour right to the end. The judge read out his sentence:

"On the first count of this indictment for handling stolen goods you will go to prison for three years . . . . ."

"That's alright judge, I'll do that standing on me dick."

The learned judge did not appear to hear and certainly did not react. Instead he went impassively on.

" . . . and on the second count for theft you will go to prison for three years (long pause) to run consecutively (further long pause) and perhaps that will put you back on your feet."

63. Heavenwards

After his appointment as Lord Chancellor in 1997, Lord Irvine of Lairg became very aware of the great extent of his powers, not restricted to those afforded by the holding of that high office. Though perhaps better known for the extravagant cost of Pugin wallpapers he caused to be imported into his official residence, he compared himself, in power, position and influence, with Cardinal Thomas Wolsey. Unlike Wolsey, however, there is no evidence that he ever aspired to become Pope. None the less, to the consternation of many, he authorised the installation of a shop in the Royal Courts of Justice. Trade within the precincts of that hallowed place! This moved His Honour Judge John Weeks QC to write to The Times:

"Sir, I see the Lord Chancellor is to sell key-rings and mouse-mats in theRoyal Courts of Justice (leading article July 10th 2000). How long before he sells pardons and indulgences?"

64. Jargon

A fledgling barrister received instructions to defend one accused of handling stolen goods, which consisted of ceramic hand washing basins taken originally by the thief from a builder's yard. His chambers did little criminal work and he was perhaps somewhat unworldly. Certainly he was not familiar with some jargon of the underworld. In the course of the trial it was said that the accused had tried to dispose of the goods, but came up against those who knew the form.

"No thanks mate, its all bent."

Counsel went on with lovely precise diction.

"Did we hear you say bent?"

"Yes."

"Spelt B E N T ?"

"I suppose so."

"Please then explain for the benefit of the court how ceramic basins, which you see here as exhibit one, can be described as, or actually be, bent?"

The problem persisted in his legal career. Words like *laches*, *mesne*, *seisin*, *chose-in-action* and *mortmain* he knew: imported from the Norman French, they had been in the student's real property (real estate) textbooks. In the fullness of time however he became a Recorder. From his cloistered existence in the civil law he found himself again faced with jargon of the underworld. They got me 'bang to rights' was an expression the meaning of which was not linguistically immediately obvious but the context usually made it tolerably clear; without scope for argument, contest or denial. He knew better the expression: 'It's a fair cop guv'nor'.

Into a possession of drugs trial came oblique reference to equipment associated with 'chasing the dragon'. Fearful of ridicule, in the nature of not knowing who Gazza was, for he had not the faintist idea of what that meant, the Recorder had to make lunchtime inquiries to discover that this was a reference to the heating of heroin so as to produce a vapour, which could be inhaled.

The use of Latin in the law of England brought for many lawyers problems of much wider scope and significance: too great for more than mention here. For a book of reference, information and entertainment see *Lawyers' Latin* by John Gray. New edition.

'Bang to Rights' Norman Mansbridge

65. Industrious insect

In 1987 Lord Mackay of Clashfern became Lord Chancellor. Brought from Scotland by Margaret Thatcher, his brief was to implement radical reforms in most aspects of the operation and administration of English law, the majority of which would almost certainly be resisted by Bench and Bar alike in England. It is not intended here to consider any of these reforms. The standpoint of the protagonists on all contentious issues is set out in a 275 page book published by The General Council of the Bar in 1989: entitled *The Quality of Justice – The Bar's Response*.

Lord Mackay proved to be a determined and formidable adversary. Further, as an able and canny Scot, he managed his Department's finances with great efficiency and frugality. In the course of what turned out to be a running conflict there came a time (so the probably apocryphal story goes) when he invited some dignitaries of the law to meet him for informal discussions about grave and weighty matters over a cup of tea.

The tea arrived on a tray with elegant bone china cups and saucers and a small plate for each person present. On each plate was a scone with a little butter and a very small helping of honey.

"Gracious . . . ." said one of the visitors, forgetting himself for a moment as his eye fell upon the honey on his plate, " . . . Lord Chancellor I see you keep a bee."

66. Nil desperandum

There is an old chestnut, apocryphal perhaps, told variously of some of those great giants of the English Bar, whose exploits fascinated the public. They were the pop stars of the early part of the

20th century. Sir Edward Marshall Hall KC, Sir Rufus Isaacs KC, Sir Edward Carson KC, Sir Patrick Hastings K.C and others. Those were the days of capital punishment. The public thrived on the macabre question of 'to hang or not to hang'. The press fed their craving and splashed lurid details of every murder trial all over their newspapers. The great leaders of the day, engaged in these trials, became famous and household names, fashionable and influential; able to speak to judges in a manner which would be frowned upon today (in AD 2010). Sometimes in the judges was perhaps an element of envy and a desire, where possible, to ensure that these illustrious ones did not get too big for their boots.

A small and delightful book, *Six Great Advocates* (written by Lord Birkett, [himself, as Norman Birkett K.C, one of the great advocates of the 20thcentury] and published by Penguin Books in 1961) tells of some of these paragons.

So, it is said, there was an occasion when one of these great men (we shall take it for present purposes to have been Sir Edward Marshall Hall) addressed a three judge Court of Appeal.

' . . . addressed a three judge Court of Appeal'. William Papas

75

As he was opening the case for the appellant, that is telling the judges what it was all about and outlining the law upon which he would rely to found entitlement in his client, sudden interruption stopped him in his tracks. One of the Lord Justices sought to take him to task in a less than courteous manner.

"Sir Edward your contentions are unarguable, not to say utter rubbish. I really can't listen to more."

Sir Edward paused momentarily, said nothing in response then, unmoved, carried on. Some minutes later the same judge interrupted again, in a louder voice.

"Sir Edward, perhaps you did not hear me before so I will repeat myself. Your contentions are unarguable, not to say utter rubbish. Nothing that you have said since I last spoke makes any difference to this. I can't listen to more."

Sir Edward did this time respond.

"I did indeed hear your Lordship's first interrupton and understood his view, which with respect is not mine. My submissions accordingly have since been, and now *a fortiori* will be, directed to your two fellow judges."

History, or perhaps myth, does not relate whether or not Sir Edward won his appeal.

67. Short Notice

It is some years since the Companies Court, presided over by a Chancery judge, sat in open court on Monday mornings. For those instructed to appear it should have been a sinecure, money for old rope: and for those who knew what to do, it was just that. It involved reading out a form of words adapted only slightly to the case in question and asking for an order, which it was compulsory for the court to make and which would lead to winding up of the company concerned. An example from the memory of a seasoned practitioner and later judge is as follows:

"This is a petition by Her Majesty's Commissioners of Inland Revenue based on a debt of £1,000,000 for unpaid PAYE and NIC.

The list is negative and, so far as I am aware, the company does not appear. And I ask Your Lordship for the usual compulsory order."

For those very junior, instructed at the eleventh hour (as was so often the case) and who did not know what to do, it was an unnerving experience. The court was always full to overflowing, heaving with legal humanity; standing room only, jostling and pulsating beneath a mass of wigs ranging from the old, grey and greasy to the brand new pristine white. All who apparently knew the form and were likely en masse to ridicule one who plainly didn't.

Two perhaps apocryphal episodes explain. In each the brief was indeed delivered at the eleventh hour, that is shortly before court on Monday morning to the greenest of young barristers.

In the first somebody provided the formula to be read and assured him that it was a piece of cake. He need do nothing more. He worried that there must be more to it than that and was reluctant to utter what was to him a largely meaningless incantation. It seemed too easy and too good to be true to warrant legal attendance by so many at court? In a lather of apprehension he pushed his way into the terrifying heaving mass of bewigged bodies already there. He had not had time to look at the list outside court so as to determine when his case might be called on.

The judge entered grandly and proceedings got off to a flying start. Suddenly he heard the name of his case. It was being called and he was not ready. Then in a faltering scarcely audible voice he uttered the necessary magic words, asked for the usual compulsory order . . . and hoped for the best.

"And what order exactly is it that you ask?" inquired the judge. The long silence was awful. Then:

"My Lord, I don't know."

Amongst the assembled company there was a kindness and perhaps too many others, young and old, who did not know either: there was no laughter in court! In memory he felt that he should have been grateful that the judge did not go on and rub it in with the further questions:

"Identify for me please the list which you tell me is negative?" and/or "is there an unusual compulsory order?"

But the judge made the order as asked, whatever it was.

In the other case the brief came so late that the recipient juggled with the papers, trying to read them while jogging across the zebra crossing in front of the main entrance to the Royal Courts of Justice. He was lucky to escape collision with a motor cycle (several of Her Majesty's dozy judges, relying carelessly on their right to be accorded precedence, have come to grief on that crossing). He robed at double quick speed having now learned that he was to oppose the usual compulsory order, which would be asked for in his case. How on earth did he do that? Late, he squeezed into the heaving mob and almost immediately his case was called. Someone somewhere, chanted the necessary incantation and asked for the usual compulsory order. Blind panic had by now set in.

"My understanding is that this order is to be opposed?" said the judge looking around.

"Is there anyone here to do so?"

Not a very tall man our unhappy barrister was not readily seen at the rear of the throng but he drew attention by shouting and raising a hand.

"Yes Mr . . .eh . . . Grounds?" asked the judge.

Counsel's blank mind knew of no grounds but said something.

" I oppose the usual compulsory order for all the usual reasons."

For a moment a scowling judge appeared to detect humorous insolence, indeed contempt. He gave no appearance of suffering impudent fools gladly. Then a smile appeared. Possibly he admired what might be panic resource and gave the benefit of doubt.

"Instructed late?"

He did not wait for an answer.

"I'll adjourn this case and will hear you later in the morning when, it is to be hoped that you will give me more specific grounds for opposing the order asked."

68. Learning curve

On the staircase of, and above, a set of chambers in the Temple, into which a young barrister had been taken for his pupillage, was a residential flat where lived a peer of the realm, when he was not in his baronial castle. The young man had passed this fellow on the stairs once or twice. He was a big man who looked very fierce and did not acknowledge the pupils who came and went and trafficked his staircase for but a short time.

His pupil master and the junior members of the chambers were however thoughtful and less forbidding and, shortly before Christmas, invited him one evening to go with them for a drink: on the strict understanding (for which, in the event he was extremely grateful) that no drink should on any account be bought or even offered by him.

It was his first experience of El Vino. A wine bar at 47, Fleet Street established in 1879, it had a reputation for fine, if expensive, wines and therapeutic oblivion. Festive Christmas spirit burst out of the door: the place was full to overflowing with cheery bodies: all abuzz: merriment, laughter and the unique loud noise of mass drink-animated conversation transcended by non-stop popping of champagne corks. Those were the days before the journalists left for pastures new. Surprisingly perhaps lawyers and journalists produced a heady mix.

His companions managed to squeeze their way into this cauldron of festive elation and they bought Veuve Clicquot and more Veuve Clicquot, hardly compatible with the still prevailing wartime austerity reflected in the Phillips stick-a soles and the steel tipped heels of his shoes. He joined little in the conversation then, aware suddenly of a light-headedness, stepped unsteadily and heavily backwards only to feel the steel tip of his heel crunch deep into the toe of an unknown. Covered in embarrassed confusion and sympathy he turned, apology ready, to face an expected aggrieved. He met instead with a broad smile.

"Dear boy, do not distress yourself and please do not apologise. Entirely my fault. You see I have such very big feet."

Suddenly it was time to go. What a civilised memory to treasure. He took leave of his generous hosts, who left for home, while he lurched unsteadily back to chambers to collect his bag.

Spreadeagled across the three steps at the foot of the stairs, lying on his back was none other than the peer of the realm. He appeared to breathe: not dead! What to do? Get an ambulance? Go upstairs to the phone? As he picked a way slowly and with infinite care over the prostrate body and through a veritable thick cloud of whisky vapour, he noticed an open eye.

"What do you think you're doing young man? Can't you see that I can't get up?"

69. Russian connection

In 1962–3, when hostility and mistrust ran high still in the cold war with the USSR (the Union of Soviet Socialist Republics) the Secretary of State for War in Prime Minister Harold Macmillan's conservative government was D-Day hero John Profumo. His upper class connections took him to upper crust parties thrown at Cliveden by Lord Astor. There he met a young woman called Christine Keeler whose allure he found irresistible and led him into fateful indiscretion. As more and more came to light, scandal built up. The newspapers had a field day. Yet he continued to deny. The plot thickened however as even more was revealed daily by the excited media. His denial was refuted and it emerged that Miss Keeler was also having a relationship with a Russian diplomat, one Captain Yevgeny Ivanov.

Having misled the Prime Minister over the nature of his relationship, he was forced to resign. Other inter-related unfortunate events complicated the huge scandal, which entranced the nation. All this is not relevant here save that events led to a criminal trial (not of Mr Profumo) at the Old Bailey (The Central Criminal Court) in which Christine Keeler was to give evidence.

These events and machinations were a source of considerable legal and human interest as well as having national security significance. Each day the revelations of the press were much discussed by barristers, young and old, over lunch in their Inns of Court.

When the Old Bailey trial was underway and Miss Keeler about to give evidence, one young barrister announced that he proposed to go to the Bailey next day to see for himself this siren, irresistible to men, who was central in the dramatic shemozzle, which had developed and rocked the nation.

He was not into lunch next day but turned up the day after.

"Well did you go to the Bailey?" asked a colleague.

"I did."

"Did she give evidence?"

"She did."

"And did you see her do so?"

"Yes."

"Well what have you to report to us?"

"My personal verdict, as a man of the world, is that you really can't blame the poor old Minister for War . . . pity about the Russian connection!"

'Royal Courts of Justice'.
William Papas

83

70. Latin in the law

In January of 1999 the Lord Chief Justice of England , Lord Woolf (as he then was) spearheaded a campaign for abolition of the use of Latin in the language of the law. He had already arranged for it to be virtually eliminated from the then new Civil Procedure Rules (CPR) replacing the Rules of the Supreme Court with effect from 26th April 1999.

Broadly the objective was to help public understanding of the legal process. Against that many Latin expressions are no more than labels attaching to concepts in, or branches of, the law: the tools of the trade. There is little need for public understanding. Lawyers seldom use them when advising lay clients. There are arguments for and against the law's continued use of Latin but here is not the place to air them.

As long ago as 1730 (as is pointed out in Professor Glanville William's book *Learning the law*, which has served students of law for many years) an Act was passed abolishing use of Law Latin in legal proceedings. The ban was short lived. Latin was found to be too ingrained and indispensable and after two years another Act was passed permitting the continued use 'in the same language as hath been commonly used.'

Today's ban has never been fullyy observed. See eg., *Arthur J.S.Hall and co. v Simons* [2000] 3 WLR 543 p 557 et seq. (House of Lords the then final appellate court). Sometimes this was seen (rightly or wrongly) as resistance to what was seen as unnecessary and obstructive. More probably it was the unconscious habit of older lawyers reflecting convenient use of another language, with which they were familiar, to pin-point what they wanted to say.

As part of our heritage Latin seems to be slipping back. See *Harding v Wealands* [2006] UKHL 32) where the speeches of two Lords of Appeal in Ordinary [Law Lords] were sufficiently studded with Latin as to justify talk of revival. In 2009 a law lord sitting in the Privy Council did not hesitate to use the 'maxim' *res ipsa loquitur* (the thing speaks for itself or the thing itself speaks) see *George v Eagle Air Services Ltd and Others.* The Times 15th May 2009. Lord Hoffmann, with a background in Roman-Dutch law from South Africa, was able, when he found use of a Latin phrase apt, to find a legal loophole enabling him to distinguish the anti-Latin ban and properly to avoid blatant contravention of the decree. Thus in *Dimond v Lovell* [2000] 2 WLR 1121 p.1131.2 he found the expression *res inter alios acta* irresistible and, immediately after using it, regularised his position with exculpatory words 'as one used to say.'

Res inter alios acta alteri nocere non debet is the full version of the abbreviation used by Lord Hoffmann and translates as 'a matter concluded between other persons ought not to hurt (disadvantage) someone else' meaning a person ought not to be prejudiced by matters transacted between others.

71. First Case

Appointment to Assistant Recorder used to be the first step on the judicial ladder. It was however a precarious step. Seen as probationary, it gave no security of tenure. The holder of the office could be instantly dismissed without reason given at the whim of an autocratic Lord Chancellor's Department. The position did however involve what was termed 'the despatch of judicial business' (not apparently the dispensing of justice!) and the absence of any security of tenure meant a constant looking over the shoulder lest the holder of the office offend, perpetrate some basic error or show himself unforgivably out of touch so as to jeopardise his future with a black mark and an adverse entry in the Lord Chancellor's secret files.

Usually there was promotion to full recorder (when for the first time the judicial oath was taken . . . 'to do right to all manner of people after the laws and usages of this realm without fear or favour affection or illwill' – [sic]. (Supreme Court Act 1981 10(4) read with Section 4 Promissory Oaths Act 1868) . . . after not less than three years if adjudged suitable and competent. This was not automatic. Some were allowed to soldier on for some time at the lesser rates of remuneration before either finally being promoted to full recorder, with its three year *prima facie* security of tenure (renewable from time to time for the same duration at the discretion of the Lord Chancellor and subject to continuing good behaviour) or very direct termination, services no longer required. This state of affairs provided no judicial independence of the executive (something of basic constitutional importance even at this lowest level) and the position of Assistant Recorder was for this reason abolished in 2000.

A barrister, made Assistant Recorder circa 1984 tells of his experience: "On day three as 'new-boy' judge I had to preside over my first contested trial: hitherto I had dealt with applications and sentencing on pleas of guilty. Though treated with much charm by a handsome and efficient lady clerk, I had not become used to being addressed as 'Your Honour': even though appreciation of this sudden grandeur had been substantially diluted by a persisting apprehension. I was not a criminal lawyer and, anxious to avoid error borne of ignorance, had caused some administrative consternation by insisting that I have the papers the night before trial: that I might swot up generally and appear on top of things whilst seeking only to avoid humiliation, which I was convinced was in the offing.

The case turned out to be very simple. It involved possession of drugs. The accused had been seen to hide them after which they were seized by watching police, who almost immediately after arrested him. Drugs had been analysed but no prospective evidence in the statements showed that those analysed were the ones seized. Elementary I thought and confidently expected a notice of further evidence to be produced identifying who had labelled the drugs found, handed them over to the analyst and taken charge of them for exhibiting after analysis.

At ten twenty five the lady clerk arrived to escort me into court. I dreaded the sound of her approaching footsteps.

"I have been asked to tell Your Honour that it is the first contested case of the young lady counsel defending."

"Mine too! Am I asked to look after her?"

"I have no further instructions."

What diplomacy. The blind leading the blind, I thought and seemed to remember from St. Matthew (15:14) that 'both shall fall into the ditch.'

"Is Your Honour ready?" she asked and offered to carry my books and papers. Of course I declined. No gentleman would permit such a thing

I nodded assent to readiness, then followed her at a brisk pace along a corridor until we met a blank door which she threw open announcing:

"Court will be upstanding."

I just wanted to go home but walked briskly and purposefully (as bid on the inauguration course) to my seat where the assembled company below responded to my bow.

Prosecuting Counsel was an untidy looking overweight fellow. Defending was a stunning young woman: tall, slender, elegant with fine facial features and lovely dark complexion: probably Somali, I thought. The defence did not seem promising to me: identity? The accused had been arrested within moments of hiding the gear, albeit that he was momentarily out of sight and immediately raised a denial. That is the prosecution case said counsel at last, closing his case. Defence counsel rose to her feet.

"I call the defendant" she announced.

"I think that I should first ask prosecuting counsel some questions, please sit down." I said.

The jury retired.

The prosecuting fellow stood up.

"I have been expecting a notice of further evidence because nothing shows that the drugs analysed and exhibited are those hidden and taken by police." I said.

There was no such notice and no apology. In progressively repetitive and vehement bluster he maintained that an inference was to be drawn; it was quite obvious.

"The jury took an oath to give a verdict *according to the evidence*. On this aspect of the case there is no evidence." I said.

He started again on the same tack and the scarcely concealed inference now seemed to be that I was stupid and unreasonable. I stopped him.

"If you are not able to point to EVIDENCE sit down!"

"Is there anything you would like to say?" I asked defence counsel, adding that I proposed to direct the jury to bring in a verdict of not guilty.

She rose slowly and majestically to her full and elegant height. She looked so formidable, cross and fierce.

"Yes" she replied.

I was suddenly unnerved. She continued to look at me with penetrating brown eyes but said nothing. My heart dropped into the pit of my stomach. "Oh Gawd" I thought, "she's a feminist". I'd rather taken over: walked roughshod all over her. She'd complain to the Lord Chancellor's Department. Whatever my explanation there would be no smoke without fire and an inevitable black mark on the secret files. My first trial! She didn't speak still. I pulled myself somehow together.

"Very well, please tell us what you would like to say?"

"I would just like to say that I agree with all that Your Honour has been saying."

72. *Celebrity*

Many in 2010 will not remember Gazza. Some years ago, at the height of his footballing fame, a judge in open court was unwise enough to ask who he was. At the time he was on a par with the likes of David Beckham, Wayne Rooney, Andy Murray or Rafael Nadal in 2010. All hell broke loose. The media had a field-day. Judges were dinosaurs, fuddy-duddies dangerously out of touch with the real world: with elitist education more familiar with Horace and Homer and the playing fields of Eton: utterly ill-equipped to understand and deal with the average man in the street. To far too many people, not to know such a thing, was unbelievable: very bad for the judicial image. So it became of paramount importance to avoid gaffes (if a straight-forward and honest declaration of ignorance be properly so described) of this kind if earthly possible. As ever the burden was heaviest upon the most vulnerable, the bottom of the pile judiciary, the Recorders and, in earlier times Assistant Recorders. Any such blunder could jeopardise their position or prospects of advancement.

At heavy handed interview before appointment, by a senior official of the Lord Chancellor's Department, it was customary for an aspiring judge to be asked: "Is there anything in your life which you think might embarrass the Lord Chancellor and which you think you ought to tell us?"

"I have no speeding or other convictions and I have learned who Gazza is: I did when inebriated as an undergraduate, forgive me, piss over Balliol. I've never really understood why. It was just the done thing: particularly en masse by drunken rugger players", answered one man. This did not seem entirely to be appreciated. He left with the impression that it was of paramount importance to avoid ridicule and felt it incumbent upon himself to learn the names of leading footballers, cricketers, racing drivers, golfers, tennis stars, actors, actresses, pop stars etc. But with a busy practice this meant research for which there was never time.

In due course, sitting as Recorder, he presided over the trial of one whose premises had been raided by police looking for drugs. "You must be Jeremy Beadle," allegedly said the ostensibly surprised proprietor as policemen swarmed in from every direction. When he came to give evidence, he confirmed that that was indeed what he had said.

"How do you spell that name?" asked the learned Recorder forgetting himself for a moment as he wrote furiously to get down the evidence (he should have written it phonetically). There was a momentary pause. The accused's face broke into a leering grin of triumph as he leaned out of the witness box towards the Recorder.

"You don't know who he is, do you?"

Alarm bells rang. The answer was swift but unattractively authoritarian and evasive. The Recorder had indeed not faintest idea of who this man was. But no admission must be made.

"I am afraid that you are not permitted to ask me questions."

The local paper, my God, in the current climate, even the national press. He needed something more: exculpatory. It came to him as from a machine in a Greek play (adopted in Latin; *deus ex machina* 'god from a machine'. A god introduced by machinery frequently appeared at the end of Greek plays to sort things out) as he addressed the court and added: "But just in case there is anyone present who does not know, you tell us."

Nobody was deceived. But the press was stymied.

Jeremy Beadle was a prankster who in the 1980s popped up to surprise all at the end of his TV programme (called 'You've been Framed') broadcast at a time when counsel/Recorder would generally not yet have arrived home.

73. Clothing

Court and inter barrister language can sometimes be for the initiated only. A word or two also about their clothing would not come amiss. In the 1960s it was still customary for many barristers to wear bowler hats and striped trousers with black jacket and waistcoat. As well as being traditional, the latter were an economy measure: the jacket would take far longer to wear out than the trousers, each of which could be replaced quite separately: striped trousers often as apparently pristine but still second hand cast offs from Moss Bros' wedding hire. Silly and wasteful to throw away a good suit solely because only part of it had become unserviceable. This was perhaps a hangover from the 'waste not' thinking of wartime, not long past. The 'Younger Man's Shop' at Harrods looked to the future with very good and modestly priced charcoal grey plain worsted suits.

In court it was required that beneath the gown a white shirt with a waistcoat or a double-breasted suit be worn. This was later relaxed and a coloured shirt was permitted, provided still that, beneath a white wing collar and tabs, it was largely covered by a waistcoat or double breasted suit.

Anathema to some disciplinarian judges was the sight of an expanse of shirt in the area of the chest and upper abdomen. Judicial disapproval of contravention of this requirement was traditionally expressed by the words "I can't see you Mr . . . ." Trial would not commence until the situation had been remedied.

A Recorder was faced with this problem in the Crown Court. He did not use the conventional words. He merely adjourned as late as lunchtime and asked the usher to summon the young barrister to his private room.

"It does not trouble me greatly but you know the profession's requirement and I have to confess that on view is a very considerable expanse of white shirt covering an apparently expanding middle."

"Your Honour has it. You see I have got awfully fat recently and my waistcoat doesen't fit me any more."

"Well it is a matter for you: I've warned you. There are those higher up than I to whom it does matter. I do not propose to adjourn this trial and waste a lot of public money. For the moment just do your best to hide all that shirt from view. Thereafter more cloth covering somehow."

The young man pleaded awareness of his shortcomings, apologised and undertook to take unspecified remedial steps.

In the courts those appearing should know that to be judicially interrupted and told:

"I (we) hear what you have to say, is there anything more you wish to add" means that you are probably going to lose the case and cause irritation by saying more. Fine judgement is needed if persistence is elected: however, most clients, alas, expect a fighter who presses on regardless.

The words 'with respect' usually indicate disagreement and, used to a judge or an opponent, render acceptable what is often in effect rudeness: as where counsel explains to a judge why a standpoint adopted by him or her is idiocy.

In chambers itself tangential minds can be encountered. "I have this case about camera lense grinding . . . ." said one member to another, hoping to get some help. He was interrupted before he got near the point.

"Bound to say I've never ground a lense, save possibly by mistake under my heel."

Reverting to clothing a young barrister arrived out of the snow and ice one freezing winter morning wearing a newly acquired very smart duffle coat, bought at Harrods. He walked into the eminent Queen's Counsel head of his chambers. They chatted for a few moments about the weather as the latter eyed the new garment.

"And what is this?" he said at last.

"A duffle coat, very fashionable and very warm in this weather."

"And what are these?" asked the senior man, pointing to one.

"Called toggles, buttons made from polished antler horn. Very fashionable too."

A long pause followed as assessment was finalised and the conversation concluded with a verdict.

"Well I hope that it is a garment we don't see here very often."

Insufficiently conservative apparel for the times.

74. Slip of the Tongue

The rush hour crush on London's underground accounts for regular indecent assaults as the inevitable firm body to body pressure stimulates dirty old men. In a groper's paradise hands stray in search of ecstatic delight in forbidden zones. Those molested are outraged. At the same time, in such conditions, there is real danger that *bona fide* complainants may wrongly accuse the innocent.

One of these cases came for trial in the Crown Court. The complainant young woman described the appallingly crowded conditions on the westbound Central Line during the evening rush hour. People were so packed together that "you could feel the breath of those around". Suddenly, she said, she was horrifyingly aware of the straying hand of a tall and elegant man who stood facing her. "Sir, stop that" she said, loud, clear and indignant, alerting the whole carriage to her outrage. "Oh madam" said the man, smooth and aloof, "wishful thinking I do assure you."

At the trial which ensued the defence had it that the man's words quite obviously reflected the situation, which was an inevitable consequence of the awful travelling conditions, a point much weakened by the good looks of the young woman involved. The prosecution maintained that their use was a very deliberate ruse

93

'Could feel the breath of all around'. Norman Mansbridge

thought up in advance to mitigate risk in adventure, indecent and illegal.

The trial meandered to a close. The judge was elderly and apparently rather bored. He had heard so much like this so often before. Languidly, after the essential legal technicalities (the burden and standard of proof etc.), he came in his summing up to summary of the evidence. Of prime importance in fairness to the accused was to set the scene by emphasising the conditions in the carriage to which human beings were subjected. He glanced at his notebook and went on: "imagine sardines squashed into a tin, not unlike humanity compressed in the confines of the London under-ground carriage with which you are concerned. In this awful crush you could feel the breasts of all around . . ." "Your Honour, 'breath' was the word used in evidence" said counsel and the foreman of the jury, each springing to their feet. "Indeed it was. Thank you . . . yes . . ." said His Honour, apparently unmoved ". . . feel the **breath** of all around, members of the jury. . . " he continued, his nonchalance belied by the bright scarlet red of his cheeks contrasting with the (tyrian?)* purple of his robes.

75. Recoveries

Recoveries used to provide a substantial part of many young common law barrister's staple diet. The process was in the nature of debt collection. Insurance companies, who had paid out their insured, sought reimbursement from third parties at fault in causing damage to their insured's vehicle. Counsel would be instructed to go to the appropriate County Court and secure a judgment against the defaulter for the appropriate amount from the County Court Judge.

* tyrian . . . purple of the Roman Emperors.

A necessary part of this operation was proof of the damage and that the cost of repair was fair and reasonable. Technically this could only be properly done by calling as a witness a fitter from the garage where repair had been effected, who was familiar with and could speak as to, what had been done and the proper and reasonable cost thereof. Fitters were usually reluctant to attend court, since their time could be more remuneratively used elsewhere. A pragmatic practice arose of bending the rules. Most judges were willing to look at a repairer's account and give a judgement on that basis. Defendants seldom turned up to resist: if they did, this procedure was not possible. One judge however would not permit this useful, sensible and reasonable course. Counsel sought to persuade him.

"Would Your Honour look at this account? It shows a breakdown of the damage and repairs with itemised and overall cost. It is well set out and very clear."

"No. Where is your witness from the repairers to prove it and its content?"

"Your Honour I do not have one."

"Then I cannot help you."

"Your Honour it is a practice followed by your brethren in most County Courts."

"That is irrelevant when in my judgement it is not a proper course."

"Your Honour the Defendant has not seen fit to appear, fitters are reluctant to attend for reasons of remuneration and if by any chance the defendant feels himself hard done by and can properly excuse his failure to be here today, he may have the judgment set aside. No injustice will be done."

"I hear what you say. It is not a proper course and will not be allowed in my court."

"Will Your Honour not accede to the good sense of such a course?"

This was incautious.

"Have I not made it clear that it is not a proper course?"

"Do I understand that I cannot persuade Your Honour to good sense?"

Silence ensued as his honour's face went puce with rage. Accepting that the day was lost Counsel responded.

"Fair enough."

His Honour threw a wobbly.

"I am unused to being spoken to in such a way. I shall retire to contain myself and consider the appropriate action. Counsel had thought 'fair enough' a conciliatory closing expression, utterly without provocation. On return His Honour had cooled down and gave only a warning. The benches were filled to overflowing with white wigs awaiting their turn. In the weeks following our hero learned that he had become known as 'fair enough'.

Some lawyers acquire nick-names. Here are some . . . Black Jack, bullying manner, owly (attributable perhaps more to his spectacles than to himself), and that fashionable defamation solicitor who endured an unhappy but predictable schoolboy distortion of his name: Peter Carter-Ruck with an F.

A judge who uses any one or more of the expressions following is suspect:

'I am much obliged (thank you very much or I'm very grateful), it matters not (it doesn't matter), abundantly clear (very clear indeed), not one jot or tittle (the least bit) not one scintilla of evidence (not a shred of evidence).

76. Supermarket

Ladies of a certain age and unconscious charm have a way with policemen. One walked from a supermarket with her basket of recent purchases only to be stopped by a woman security officer. It was said that a stick loaf under her arm was unpaid for and stolen.

"Gracious" she replied.

"You may be right. I might not have paid for it but I have certainly not stolen it. You see my wire basket was full so I put the bread under my arm and it was presumably overlooked at checkout. It was just where it is now: so awfully visible. The girl might have charged for it even though I forgot to draw her attention to it. Just a moment: let me look at my bill. No, it isn't there. But that's alright, I'll pay for it now of course."

"Sorry madam. Too late. This is a police matter now."

The lady was unceremoniously shepherded into an office inside the store. The police were summoned and duly arrived. The security officer made her allegations. The police officer solemnly read to her the required caution (old style): "you are not obliged to say anything unless you wish to do so . . . .". The accused stood silent and bewildered in front of and staring at him. " . . . but what you say may be put into writing and given in evidence."

She had taken in nothing of what he had said.

"Officer, I should tell you that your hat is not on straight."

Her diplomat son, waiting outside in the car had noticed the time she took, looked for and found her. He managed to persuade all concerned to good sense.

A lady of like age was hailed by a policeman and stopped.

"This is a one-way street, madam." he declared, somewhat menacingly.

"Well officer, can't you see, I'm only going one way?"

An experienced Crown Court Judge has declared himself terrified of this kind of episode and declines utterly ever to enter a supermarket.

77. *Happy encounter*

Her majesty's High Court Judges go on circuit: that is leave London and travel to local courts to preside over the more serious cases. In the days of the assize they sat in specified towns as the Queen's (or King's) representatives under their commissions of oyer and terminer and gaol delivery. So far as crime was concerned this meant that those accused were kept in prison until Her Majesty's judge arrived in the town when they were released from gaol to be tried and then discharged or, too often. hanged.

Judges on these occasions stay often for several weeks and reside in the judge's lodgings where they are fed and live in considerable luxury, the cost of which is complained about from time to time by politicians. However judges can scarcely be seen to rub shoulders in a hotel with, solicitors, counsel, jurymen, defendants and witnesses.

On arrival a judge will be met by the lodgings butler, shown his bedroom and told when meals will be served. A certain judge walked round surveying the bedroom and sat on the very big bed, testing the mattress. Then he pulled back the counterpane. There followed a silence as the eye of both fell upon something under the pillow. His Lordship put down a hand and pulled it out. A lady's black nightdress unrolled itself, full length. Pure silk, lovely to touch. Neither spoke. Explanation was not obvious. The butler did not have one and didn't offer and her ladyship did not accompany her husband. His Lordship folded it slowly up. The butler stood fearful of his reaction.

"I think that you should take this garment away" he said at last and expressionless handed it over. As the butler departed he added:

"Just bring it back filled up." His face had broadened into a smile.

78. Good settlement?

Lawyers in all areas of the law frequently find it prudent to compromise and settle their cases. Usually this saves their client expense and certainly eliminates the risk of disastrous total loss inherent in litigation hazard. It can be a very skilled business for it is necessary to persuade one's opponent of the strength of one's case and the weakness of his. It is a game often of bullshit and counter bullshit, bluff and counterbluff: something of a game of poker.

In advance of trial there are those fearful of their prospects and desperate to settle but who notwithstanding will not lift the telephone to initiate the necessary negotiation. That would show lack of confidence in his prospects and weakness of character. One has to keep one's nerve and, as in a game of poker, hide one's reservations. At the end of the day both parties hope to come away with the one thinking 'I gave too much' while his opponent thinks 'I took too little'.

There is advice and warning from antiquity. *Esto consentiens adversario tuo cito dum es in via cum eo: ne forte tradat te adversarius judici, et judex tradat te ministro: et in carcerem mittaris*' be at agreement with thine adversary quickly whilst thou art in the way [still on speaking terms] with him: lest perhaps the adversary deliver thee to the judge, and the judge deliver thee to the officer and thou be cast into prison.' Vulgate. St. Matthew, 5.25. St. Matthew was plainly aware of the possible dire consequences of not settling. Plautus too warned: *'quam meticulosa res sit ire ad judicem* 'you don't know what a terrible thing it is to go to the judge'.

In the UK the death penalty was finally abolished in 1999. No longer may a judge in our courts have to don the macabre black cap and speak those terrible words: "the sentence of this court upon you is, that you be taken from this place to a lawful prison, and that there you suffer death by hanging; and that your body be afterwards buried within the precincts of the prison in which you shall have been confined before execution. And may the Lord have mercy upon your soul."

The relevance of the preceding paragraphs lies in a situation to be imagined. Picture a macabre crowd gathered around a 15th century scaffold guarded by steel helmeted soldiers with their pikes and halberds. A priest stands beside a vast figure of a man clad all in black, with mask to match, looking out from sinister eye slits: he wields a mighty axe and stands threateningly over an unhappy condemned figure, kneeling, his head already on the block, not long for this world, as he awaits a swift strike and oblivion.

His little attorney, anxious to speak important last words to his wretched client, has braved the crowd and got past the soldiers and leans over the side of the scaffold, close enough and just in time to reach his client's ear. He manages a remarkable detached professional objectivity. "You have my firm assurance" he whispers "that in this matter I negotiated the best possible settlement on your behalf.'

79. Inflation

Awards of damages for personal injury, a rarity before, became increasingly common in the reign of Queen Victoria as burgeoning industry inflicted injury upon so many working men and women. There was then a great class divide. Compensatory damages tended to be very low. Unconscious judicial thinking was perhaps "I can't award so much to a fellow like that: he won't know what to do with it and will only waste it."

With the arrival of the motor car, and the ever increasing ownership of it, came endless collisions causing personal injury. The assessment and award of damages for such injury became a regular feature of the judicial function. In a system of precedent however, the following of earlier decided cases tended with time to keep such damages at an ever increasingly low level. Little or no thought was given to inflation and the ever diminishing value of money in real terms.

Only in the very late 1960s and early 1970s did this fundamental injustice start to be addressed. Circa 1973, Mr Justice O'Connor, a Queen's Bench judge then for some few years, had made no secret of his firm intention to increase, as far as he personally could, the level of general damages for personal injury, that is for pain, suffering and loss of amenity. He spearheaded a move for change. In the fullness of time this led to wide recognition of the law's deficiency in this respect and to the use of inflation tables to update awards in past cases by reflecting them in money of the day. For the 2010 position see Heil v Rankin 2001 1 QB 272. But in the transitional early seventies there opened up pitfalls for practitioners.

One young barrister pursued a claim for damages on behalf of a young man badly injured when he fell down a lift shaft. The case was not settled and came for trial. It was one of those most worrying matters where liability remained in dispute and he could not see how he could lose.

Subject to that, depending on the judge before whom it might come, he estimated general damages for pain, suffering and loss of amenity to be in the region of £10,750–£12,500 (very approximately £102,000- £119,000 in 2010).

He had not much experience of non-jury (civil) trials in the Queen's Bench Division of the High Court and was distinctly nervous. So far as damages were concerned he was pleased: the matter had been listed before Mr Justice O'Connor.

Outside court he met his opponent for the defendant insurers, a considerably more senior barrister, one Michael Ogden (later Sir Michael Ogden QC).

"Liability will not be contested . . ." the latter announced abruply after introductions ". . . only quantum of damage remains."

So great was the relief of no contest on liability, that this was immediately countered with a certain air of triumph: an unfriendly professionalism having suggested to him that he was considered as so much potential putty in the hands of the more senior man.

"You have no money in court. Are you therefore going to make an offer?"

"As general damages for pain, suffering and loss of amenity you may have £10,000." (£95,000 very approximately in 2009) he said suddenly, after probing unsuccessfully for what figure was asked.

The plaintiff was advised: there is no money in court, liability is conceded, so you run no risk as to costs. It is conceivable that you could get less than £10,000 but with this judge it is highly unlikely. At a guess more will be offered, perhaps even before court starts. It had to be a matter for him. £10,000 was a lot of money but the advice was to refuse it.

He duly refused and this was conveyed to Mr Ogden. At that moment an agitated clerk of the lists appeared. Mr Justice O'Connor was unwell and would not be sitting that day. The case was now a floater but, with a bit of luck, another judge would shortly be assigned. He was. Mr Justice Hinchcliffe. Recently he had found for the plaintiff's barrister at the Maidstone assize: and was seen as likeable, but one of the old brigade about to retire. What he was like on damages was unknown but seemed for the plaintiff too great a risk. Advice had him agree to take £10,000 after all.

"Oh no" said Ogden "you have rejected the offer. It is no longer open." His expression suggested that he knew the damages levels of this judge as he offered £8,000.

The case was fought with zeal on both sides. Ogden was very fierce. The judge gave an *ex tempore* judgement. Breath was held as at last he came to the crucial figure.

"And I award as general damages for pain, suffering and loss of amenity the sum of seven thousand five hundred pounds."

It was a bombshell. The disaster was immense. The plaintiff would never understand why he couldn't have £10,000. His counsel was devastated.

Spero meliora 'I hope for better things': fate had dealt an unkind blow. It was to be some time before he felt able to say to himself *nunc demum redit animus* 'now at last our spirit returns.' Tacitus Agricola 3.

80. *At spes non fracta* *

Regina versus John Smith. A criminal case appeared in the pigeon hole of a barrister who was essentially a civil practitioner. "What's this?" he asked his clerk. "Bad boy relative of one of your best instructing solicitors. He asked that you take the case Sir. Sorry. I meant to ask you, but I knew you wouldn't dare say no."

The papers revealed a 'long firm fraud': one of those episodes where an ostensible business is set up in derelict premises; telephone is installed and then some irresistible postal bargain advertised. When the cheques in response come rolling in they are banked and the money withdrawn. All concerned then disappear at a carefully chosen moment when little or nothing of the promised bargain has been honoured.

The papers revealed that John Smith was used by older more sophisticated criminals whose *modus operandi* in the past, it seemed, had proved very lucrative. There appeared however to be little doubt that he knew exactly what he was at and had been handsomely rewarded for the small but crucial part he had played. There were three other defendants. The organisers of these frauds are difficult to trace and the police had worked very hard and taken great care with assembling the evidence.

Mr Smith was seen in conference. Counsel had by then read and considered all the papers. After asking for explanation of several aspects of the most damning evidence and having not received sat-

* 'but hope is not yet broken'

isfactory answers and having himself been unable to see any escape, he explained that the case against seemed overwhelming. "Yes but I'm not guilty" said Smith. Counsel tendered gently and diffidently some carefully phrased advice. "If, having thought about the matter you consider that you might be guilty, then a plea of guilty could be very beneficial. After all the part you allegedly played was small: you have no previous convictions and a lot of court time and public expense would be saved?" There was no question of thinking further about it. He was not guilty and would so plead.

The day for trial arrived: at the Old Bailey (the Central Criminal Court). The three other alleged crony accomplices were each separately represented. They all pleaded not guilty. Senior, well known prosecuting counsel had been engaged, to make sure that police efforts did not come to nothing. Smith's counsel was rather depressed. Apparently hopeless cases are always dispiriting. It is hard to look sincere as endlessly one tries to advance plausible reasons why black may be white and *vice versa*.

Half way through the morning of the third day of trial Smith went into the witness box. Already his co-accused had each suffered humiliating annihilation as their defences were demolished with great forensic skill. He gave his evidence in chief and with some trepidation awaited cross-examination. Prosecuting counsel rose slowly and menacingly to his feet and then eyed his prey for a few moments with a laser look intended to penetrate deep. Such examination would not have been difficult but it was done with consummate skill. One damning and unanswerable well phrased question relentlessly followed another and tore into their target like machine gun bullets. Smith slumped as he broke out into a visible cold sweat and guilt seemed to be ruthlessly exposed. But he never quite said "hands up. I'm guilty. No more please." Prosecuting counsel's performance was a lesson in the art: clinical, well prepared: very professional. Smith appeared a broken man. The lunch adjournment brought him relief.

In this break came a message from Mr Smith via his solicitor.

Would his brief come and see him in the cells below, please. Counsel obliged. Smith was in a terrible state, drenched in sweat and trembling visibly.

"I can't take any more of this" he said "I want to plead guilty like you said."

"Mr Smith", said counsel, "cross – examination is over. You will be subjected to no more. I can see that it has been very wearing for you. But there is little or no advantage to be gained at this late stage. You assured me that you were not guilty. Only if you tell me now that that was not true should you plead guilty at this stage. If you want just to bring to an end the kind of torment to which you have just been subjected, then I advise you to stick with your present plea and take your chance."

He paused for a little.

"OK Mister. I'll take my chance."

The heat was now on counsel. What on earth could he say that was good sense in a final speech on behalf of his client? He cut short his lunch and returned to court to consult his notes and see just how damaging had been Smith's answers given during the morning, of themselves, uninfluenced by prosecuting counsel's overbearing presence.

As he passed the jury box his eye fell upon a sheaf of juror's papers on which something had been drawn. Perhaps he shouldn't have, but he couldn't resist a look. Even upside down was readily discernible four gallows on a scaffold with four bodies hanging limp from the noosed rope attached. Oh dear, he thought.

The evidence closed that afternoon. Next day would be speeches, summing up and verdict.

That evening counsel worked late and hard to make bricks without straw. But as ever something could be said, least about the actual evidence. Prosecuting counsel's cross-examination, while masterly had perhaps overdone it. He was plainly used to vicious criminals needing rough treatment. It doesn't do to crucify any but the most unpleasant criminals. Mr Smith was much younger than the other defendants, he had no previous convictions and his part in what was a very culpable criminal enterprise was small indeed. It had not really come out how well he had been remunerated. A gentle appeal to sympathy was concealed in carefully constructed rhetoric and, spotlighted, were some of prosecuting counsel's arguably unfair, unkind and/or unnecessarily harsh observations.

He delivered his speech next day. The judge's summing up made plain his view: guilty all four. The jury retired at last. There was a long draining wait before they returned at last with verdicts upon which all were agreed. Guilty were Smith's three co-defendants. Counsel could not help but remember that in the drawing were four men dangling from hangman's nooses. This stage of a criminal trial is always nerve-racking. Smith's turn came. "On count . . . for . . . do you find John Smith guilty or not guilty?" His counsel held his breath. "Not guilty."

Mr Smith was discharged. His counsel shook his hand.

"Well Mr Smith, you were right and I was wrong."

Smith smiled, too overcome to reply.

Nil desperandum 'never give up (despair).' No case is ever utterly without hope. An English barrister is professionally obliged to take on seemingly hopeless cases. What he personally thinks is beside the point. He offers no more than to do his professional best for his client and to do what he can with the material available. If this were not so there might be those (particularly those framed) who would never be professionally defended.

81. A Military Matter

There landed one day on the desk of a young barrister a brief to defend in a matter to be heard in the 'Outlandish Magistrates Court'. The young barrister, Mr Coltart, was busy at the time and did not look inside to see what it was all about. Like so many young common law barristers his practice involved a fair share of motoring cases and, noting the name of the instructing solicitors, he assumed this to be such a case. He noted too, with some satisfaction, that it was marked with a fee (in guineas!) just a little greater than the usual insurance company backed fee, even taking account of the long distance he would have to travel to conduct the defence.

Days later, lest anything needed to be done, he slid the red tape off the brief and opened the papers. Gracious! His client to be was a young man in his mid thirties and a banker. Ex-army he had met up with some of his old comrades for a few beers. It had been an hilarious evening as one beer led to another and then to another and then to one or more too many. He remembered very little of the latter stages of that evening but found himself charged notwithstanding with dangerous driving, driving without due care and attention and driving whilst unfit through drink.

Unusually the driving had not been of his own motorcar or that of any other, but was of a tank commandeered apparently through his and/or his comrades' inside knowledge of MOD security. It had caused some consternation as, in the early hours of morning, it had rumbled, crash bang, crash bang, along the High Street of a country market town, crunching and writing off parked cars to right and left and leaving havoc in its wake. Then, horror of horrors, to make things worse, if that be possible, it had lurched off course and at speed (for a tank) into a shop, completely demolishing the door and frontage and scattering everywhere the content of the display window.

To the eternal embarrassment of terribly respectable professional parents, who, concerned, would attend court to support him, it was a sex shop! Its specialised stock had been scattered everywhere: all manner of remarkable gear, kit and equipment: to some fascinating, to others bewilderingly mysterious and to others still, emanating from such a shop, *ipso facto* disgusting!

The day came for trial. It was a long journey to the court and a wearing wait before the case was called. He had plenty of time to complete the appearance slip and wrote his name, Coltart, as he thought very clearly for the benefit of the magistrates. Following discussion with the remarkably likeable young man client, he had put together some powerful mitigation for what would inevitably be a plea of guilty. He stood up to address the bench, then paused momentarily, awaiting the chairman's invitation to speak. The latter fiddled through some papers before finding the appearance slip, looking up at counsel and opening the proceedings

"Yes Colonel Tart."

History does not relate more.

82. Under a cabbage leaf

The expression *in flagrante delicto* (more accurately without the *'in'* and translated as 'in the very act of wrongdoing') is Latin well known to many of the general public as well as to the lawyers. It is (or was, since the onslaught against use of Latin in the law commenced in about 1999) used, particularly in the courts, discreetly to identify activity otherwise described by harsher words, adultery, fornication and others less befitting the dignity of a court.

Other Latin expressions, invoked to provide a veneer of good taste, took hold in the Probate, Divorce and Admiral Division of the High Court when considering Nullity Petitions which sought to void the marriage by a decree on the basis of non-consummation at the instance of either party.

Such Petitions were too often complicated by the existence of off-spring (notwithstanding the assertion by both parties that the essential preliminaries had not taken place). These apparent virgin births were regarded with some cynicism and came to be described by the expression *fecundatio ab extra* 'by conception from outside.' The powers that be felt themselves unable to accept that there had not been some *vera copula* ('true sex') somewhere. Storks, gooseberry bushes and cabbage leaves carried no explanatory weight.

Irreverent Roman Catholics coped readily with the problem: any and all such offspring were gifts from the Holy Ghost!

83. Despot

When Her Majesty's High Court Judges go out of London on circuit, to preside over the more serious cases, they reside in special residences known as lodgings so as to ensure that they do not come up against those engaged in the cases they are trying, be they counsel, jurors or even parties to the civil litigation themselves. In the lodgings a certain protocol prevails. Life is ordered by the wishes of the senior judge in a way vaguely reminiscent of prefects' boundless authority as it used to be in public schools. This can make itself felt particularly at meal times. Some are very strong characters with very firm views. So it is said there was once a judge who was fiercely teetotal. As a junior judge he contented himself necessarily with himself not drinking at lunch and dinner. When he became a senior judge he imposed his discipline on all present. To their chagrin meals were dry.

It was customary from time to time for Recorders to be invited to lunch with the judges in the lodgings where the meal would be served by the lodgings butler. This meant a trip in the judicial cavalcade; the official chauffer driven big car with police motor-cycle escort to afford security and to clear the traffic. Strict protocol governed where who sat in the official car. Nobody must sit beside the High Court Judge.

On one such occasion a Recorder and a newly appointed circuit judge arrived for lunch in the dining room back at the lodgings. Conversation did not flow. His Lordship seemed preoccupied and did not assist. The young judge, a little overawed, groped for some affable topic with which to open the conversational batting. He guessed that, like most lawyers, His Lordship would surely wax eloquent about the case on which he was currently engaged. He broke the silence and came up with:

"Does Your Lordship try anything interesting today?"

"Indecent assault, incest, rape and buggery" came the staccato reply without more. Such a unique conversation killer ensured restoration of a very long silence.

84. Personality clash

There is a story, probably apocryphal, of a senior judge who found himself assigned to share lodgings on circuit with a relatively newly appointed judge. Since no other was to accompany them, they were destined for their own company, and since the duration of their stay was expected to be two to three weeks, he took it upon himself to make some inquiries of the junior man, who he did not know. These revealed that the latter was a very heavy smoker of cigarettes and liked a cigar at the end of dinner. This was disconcerting and prompted a letter intended to make quite clear how things were to be during their stay together. He wrote apparently in somewhat authoritarian terms along the kind of lines following:

> Dear . . . . . .
> I see that we are to be sitting at Chadcaster. The judge's lodgings there are very well appointed. I look forward to meeting you and am sure that I shall enjoy our stay, subject only to one matter. I am given to believe that you are a very heavy smoker. I do not smoke. I do not approve of smoking and have to tell you that I find the habit peculiarly disagreeable. I am unusually sensitive to the toxic smoke and detest the clinging nature

of the unpleasant smell, which it leaves behind. I must make it abundantly clear therefore that there will be no smoking anywhere inside the lodgings while we are there. Any smoking which you may find irresistible will please take place in the gardens, which are of ample size and delightful.

Yours sincerely . . . . . .

The younger man was taken aback; but whether he responded from irritation at the dictatorial tone, or from devilish humour, is speculation. Reply however he did, along the following sort of lines:

Dear . . . . .

I am in receipt of your letter. I understand completely. There need be no difficulty.

I am however given to believe that you are either unfamiliar with or indifferent to the seventh commandment. This I regret to inform you I find unhappy and contravention as unacceptable as you tell me you find smoking: I fear more so. I trust that if, during our stay, you should be seized by temptation, any consequent activity will take place please in the garden.

In the event that, while having a smoke, I should stumble across you *flagrante delicto* in the darkness, I should of course take all necessary steps not further to disturb.

With the now mutual understanding of one another's wishes, I am sure that our stay together will be most agreeable and I look forward to meeting you in Chadcaster.

Yours sincerely . . . . .

85. Excess

Police raids often discover hoards of ostensibly stolen goods of a type different from those for which they were looking. On one such occasion a search for drugs revealed a storehouse of foodstuffs and domestic materials. As this was relatively new and of very substantial value questions were asked. Satisfactory answers were not given and after some further investigation charges were brought for various theft related offences.

At trial before a judge and jury counsel for the prosecution cross-examined the occupant of the house, who was one of several accused.

"Do you usually have one hundred bottles of HP sauce in your house?"

"Quite often."

"Why?"

"'Cos we eat it, lots of it. My family really loves it and eats masses of it."

"We will come to where it comes from. But just let us get the picture. What do you say about fifty tins of Victoria plums?"

"Same. We eat them. That's pudding that is."

"And what about one hundred and twenty tins of black shoe polish?"

"Same again. We use it. All of it. Really clean shoes in our household."

And so the charade went on until:

"And what do you say about five hundred rolls of Andrex lavatory paper?"

Judge. "You need not answer that question. Counsel, please try and think ahead. In any event this line of questioning has made its point. Can we move on?"

86. Contempt?

It is axiomatic that it is as well for counsel to laugh at judges' jokes and they usually do. Claude Duveen QC (later His Honour Judge Duveen) was once addressing the Court of Criminal Appeal. He had spent a full half hour advancing a short but complex and contorted argument. One of the judges interrupted him.

"Mr Duveen, does your case not come to this . . . ?"

He produced a summary analysis in a few short sentences.

"Your Lordship puts admirably, with such succinct clarity exactly that which for so long I have been clumsily trying to advance to this court."

His Lordship smiled with discernible mildly embarrassed satisfaction.

"Thank you, Mr Duveen. You are very kind. There is no need to say that."

"I know, but one always does."

87. Driving Licence

The Hon Mr Justice Bernard Caulfield. Not a man to tangle with and not one to suffer fools gladly. Very fierce. He once drove to the town where he was due to sit at the Assize as Her Majesty's Commissioner of Oyer, Terminer and General Gaol Delivery the next morning.

A story, apocryphal perhaps, has it that en route he found himself, for no obvious reason, stopped by police. He gave his name as plain 'Bernard Caulfield' and, after a short vaguely disagreeable conversation, felt constrained to ask why he had been stopped. He suggested too, somewhat diffidently, that he had perhaps been randomly stopped and pointed out that that was something which (at that time) was not lawful and ought not to happen. At no point did he attempt to pull rank.

"You were driving erratically Mr Clever Berny Baby" said the police officer asking at the same time for a sight of the judge's driving licence. He did not have it with him: it had been left over the weekend in the judge's lodgings. "Where are you going?" asked the officer and was given the name of the town quite nearby. "Then you can produce your licence to me at the central police station tomorrow morning can't you Mr Clever Berny Baby." His Lordship did not see fit to argue though, prudently for the record, he ensured that a denial of erratic driving be recorded in the officer's notebook. He gave his name (without more) took the officer's name rank and number, wrote them on a scrap of paper and said that the licence would be produced as apparently required, the next day, and was permitted to continue his journey.

Next morning His Lordship made ready for court. Dressed in splendid scarlet robes and wig, he climbed into the official Rolls Royce car and joined the awaiting grand and bewigged retinue. There was a slight delay while a judicial directive was conveyed to the accompanying cavalcade of police motorcyclists, there to protect the grandees and to clear traffic from the route to the courts. This particular Monday morning Her Majesty's Judge at Assize and his entourage were to travel by a route different from the usual, advised ostensibly by security.

The assembled company set off and shortly after stopped suddenly outside the central police station. His Lordship in all his robed splendour emerged alone from the official car and tramped solemnly up the steps to the station entrance. At the reception desk there was some consternation as he presented a scrap of paper and asked please to see an officer of the name and number scrawled upon it. "Tell him that Mr Clever Berny Baby is here as ordered." That officer duly presented himself. Speechless he stood facing His Lordship's withering look of thunder. Nothing was said and moments later a licence was presented and handed instantly back with the apology of one who fears for his life.

88. Shredder

The old Supreme Court Practice provided (at RSC O.24) for discovery by parties to an action of all documents which are or have been in their possession, custody or power relating to matters in question in the action. These were to be listed and the lists exchanged.

Once upon a time a large engineering company was sued for damages resulting from various miscalculations made in the design and build of certain plant. A lot of money was claimed. Their in-house lawyers sought to save money by dealing themselves with an action, which they hoped and expected to be able to compromise. The plaintiffs (claimants) were however optimistic and determined and wanted their pound of flesh. No compromise for them.

As the time for trial drew near the defendant company's lawyers became nervous and went to leading counsel (a QC) for his opinion and with a view to instructing him to conduct their case should it get to court. They filled his room with lever files.

The day for consultation with counsel arrived. Four representatives of the company attended: the managing and another executive director and two in-house lawyers. After the usual introductory pleasantries counsel opened the batting.

"I have been through the voluminous documentation in all these files. It is my impression that some relevant and vital material may be missing: it is not always obvious but is detectable from what I do have. Are those in the files in this room all that you have listed and disclosed?"

The older lawyer answered.

"Yes."

"Am I right in thinking that there existed further documentation?"

The lawyer looked sideways at the managing director for the go-ahead, then answered:

"Yes."

"Do you have it still?"

"Yes."

"Where is it?"

"In a separate single lever file."

"Which I do not have. Why was it not listed and disclosed to the other side as required by the rules?"

A long pause accompanied looks of guilty discomfort. The managing director answered.

"It is very damaging to us."

For a few moments there was silence before counsel responded.

"I *dare* say there are some solicitor's shredding machines regularly red hot with user but now that I know of this documentation and its nature either you should dispose of this claim yourselves or I should see it and advise on another occasion. I do not advise use of a shredder."

89. Hard of Hearing

A lady in her eighties had been driving for over sixty years without accident or conviction. She drove each day from her little country cottage to the local village shop some two miles away. One day she drove ten miles into the big town, where her long deceased husband had been a solicitor, to buy some Christmas presents. She was sprightly and didn't look her age: she could have passed for mid sixties. Only her hearing was not good. Unhappily on her return journey, for no reason she could explain, she lost control of her little blue Peugeot car, which rode up onto the pavement and crashed into a shop window. Fortunately nobody was hurt. She herself was a little shocked but more outraged than injured. "I must have over-corrected," she asserted.

In due course she received a summons for driving without due care and attention (she was lucky it was not for dangerous driving). This upset her and she was most anxious not to lose her driving licence. She insisted on seeing a barrister. A conference was arranged at which she met a young common law barrister of an age greatly experienced in motoring offences.

He shook his head. She would have to plead guilty. But her licence? At her age, and without some extenuating explanation of how the accident happened, she was bound to lose it. No exculpating bee, wasp or hornet had flown into her car and made for her face.

"Our best, indeed only, chance, and that is a slender one" he said "is stage manageement. The hope that your age may not be noticed. If I may say so madam you do not look anything like your age. When we get to court the charge will be read and you will be asked whether you plead guilty or not guilty. You will answer 'guilty.' Leave everything else to me. Do not be drawn into any speaking. I will have taken possession of your driving licence and will do all the talking. I will not mislead them but I will hand in your licence just as I am about to address them and will hope to draw their attention from it and hence from your age. I would not be optimistic but it is in my view, I repeat, your only chance. Remember you have got to say nothing but 'guilty'. That apart, I repeat and emphasise, do not on any account be tempted to speak if you can possibly help it. I will intervene if you are spoken to."

On the due day they arrived at court. The clerk read the charge and asked her how she pleaded. He was unusually softly spoken. She did not respond for she did not hear him. There was a momentary silence while something was clearly expected of her. Before the clerk could try again she obliged. "If you want to know how old I am, I'm eighty five."

90. Old lag

A man with a very substantial criminal record was advised by his solicitor that he was on risk for about two years imprisonment for yet another series of run of the mill minor burglaries. They had him, as his colleagues would say, 'bang to rights'. The evidence against him seemed overwhelming. In his mid forties he had become institutionalised and was not too worried

But he wanted his day in court and insisted on a plea of not guilty. Quite how or why he enjoyed it was unclear, for he was substantially deaf and had very little idea of what was going on about him during a trial.

A young and keen young barrister was duly instructed to conduct his defence in the Crown Court before a judge and jury. He took one good technical point after another on behalf of the accused. Damning verbals were ruled inadmissible by the judge because the accused had not been properly cautioned at the right time, fingerprints had become muddled and a vital witness did not turn up. The prosecution case crumbled bit by bit and at the close of its case the judge accepted defence counsel's submission that there was no case to answer: and directed the jury to bring in a verdict of not guilty on his direction. He then turned to the accused.

"You are discharged and free to go."

The no longer accused looked a little bewildered then cupped an ear with a hand and addressed the judge:

"M'lud, please excuse but I didn't quite hear. How long did you give me?"

91. Causing Death

Juries were reluctant to convict drivers of motor manslaughter. The Road Traffic Act 1960 brought in a new offence, which was intended as remedy and which came to be known as 'Causing Death by Dangerous Driving'. If the driving in question created a situation which involved some fault (be it ever so small) in the driver and which as a matter of fact, looked at objectively, was dangerous, then all that remained to be proved to make out the offence was that that dangerous situation was a substantial cause of a death.

There was no question of it being necessary to show the driving to be 'dangerous' in the ordinary man's understanding, namely deliberate, intentional, reckless, antisocial: no need for *mens rea* (criminal mind or intent) generally an ingredient of any criminal offence. If a driver managed his vehicle in such a way as to create danger, it does not matter 'whether he was momentarily inattentive or even doing his incompetent best' R.v Evans 1962 3 All ER 1086 at p. 1088.

The result was, for example, that a citizen who had been driving for a very long time, sometimes 50 or more years without motor accident or conviction (and who was otherwise upright and blameless) might after an infinitesimal lapse of concentration or momentary inadvertence find himself prosecuted for, and usually convicted of, causing death by dangerous driving: and thus labelled with a conviction bearing a name suggestive to the uninitiated of iniquitous driving attracting unwarranted social stigma. The 'convict' is utterly mortified by what had happened and needs no hefty fine and compulsory disqualification from driving let alone possible imprisonment. Neither deterrent nor punishment is realistically called for.

Many of those prosecuted were outraged and insisted on a plea of not guilty and a contest before a jury, despite advice that there was no defence in law. It was not professionally easy for counsel to act as instructed, actively to seek a perverse verdict and to cope sometimes with judicial disapproval. Most judges were sympathetic and made no complaint and there were many common sense acquittals acquired by counsel's attractive review of the facts culminating in the question "are you satisfied beyond a reasonable doubt that this amounts to Causing Death by Dangerous Driving?"

The legislature has since wrestled with this problem and generated much confusion. A treatise is not here intended. Suffice it to record that with the introduction in 2009 of an offence of causing death by careless driving exactly the same problem has been reintroduced.

The bereaved in shock are seldom initially rational and often vociferously demand that someone should pay. The powers that be have pandered to their demands and too often, as the law stands, the price paid takes the form of conviction for a resoundingly serious offence (which does not reflect the facts, the moment's inadvertence) and harsh punishment for the driver leaving him with a burning sense of injustice done.

A barrister lived next door to a gentleman who was run down by his daughter as she backed the car out of his garage and across the footway outside. Fortunately her father was not killed. He received a few insignificant bruises and scratches but was more wounded by his daughter's pleaded belief that he had been the dustbin. Had he suffered injury and died, might she be guilty of causing death by dangerous driving, he wondered. It was not long before a brief to defend the real thing landed on his desk.

One frosty winters morning the accused had been backing his car out along his short drive and across the footpath outside. He was a little late and he had omitted to clear the rear window, which was frosted up. Accordingly he took it very very slowly. Suddenly there was a bump. He had gone over something and drove gently forward only to feel the bump again. He got out to find an old lady

121

prostrate on the pavement and plainly injured. She was very small and painfully thin and, bent over her stick, which lay beside her on the pavement, might well not have been visible even as a dark shadow through the frosted rear window. The old lady lingered for a few days in intensive care before she died. Hoping for a statement from her a police officer had hovered at her bedside. He recorded only her last whispered words: "he ran over me... twice."

The driver was convicted of causing death by dangerous driving.

92. Oversight

A great fear afflicting most advocates is that they should discover in the course of a trial that they have overlooked some case, principle or statute, which has a significant bearing on the matter before the court. Many have the most alarming recurring nightmares in which this has happened or in which they arrive at court totally unprepared. Of course they should continue to worry so that anxious diligence may ensure that this only rarely happens.

They may however derive comfort from the fact that notwithstanding it happens to the best. In Glebe Sugar Refining Company Ltd v Trustees of the Port and Harbours of Greenock [1921] 2 AC 66, 71 counsel (including Sir John Simon previously Attorney General and later Lord Chancellor) were forced to apologise shamefacedly for steadfastly failing to direct the attention of the Appellate Committee of the House of Lords to a relevant statutory provision.

Again, when he was Lord Justice Denning, Lord Denning observed that it was regrettable that, in an earlier case, to which he referred, the principle which he had just enunciated had not been drawn to the attention of the court. It was so much more to be regretted [as he bravely admitted] because he had himself been counsel in that earlier case! See Cassidy v Minister of Health [1951] 2 KB 342 and 363.

When he was an undergraduate at Oxford Mr C.H.S. Fifoot (co-author of that enduring work, originally Cheshire and Fifoot, The Law of Contract) was invited to attend for a *viva voce* interview by the examiners after the written papers in his final jurisprudence examination had been completed (as were all those who had qualified as possible candidates for the first class degree). One asked him about: "that fascinating case, Re the Bolivian Petrol Company, which you have cited and which illustrates so succinctly a difficult, and I'm bound to say, I thought hitherto undecided point. I have spent an eternity looking for it but am quite unable to find it. Are you able from memory please to give me some rough reference or other helpful guidance?"

This put Mr Fifoot on the spot. After some anxious hesitation, he opted to come clean. The don would never find it. The case (along with others) was fictitious, Mr Fifoot's own original creation. As he recollects: "they didn't look very pleased or amused but were not unkind to me in the end."

No need to worry about what you might have overlooked if you can make up convenient new cases as you go along.

93. Decision

One morning a commuting judge (an Official Referee as they were then known) climbed breathless into his 8.00 a.m. train bound for Charing X and crashed into a seat beside a colleague. After a little, when he had settled, the colleague observed:

"You don't look so good. Hangover?"

"No, no. never drink during the week."

"Worse than your usual panic attacks on the drive to the station ? . . ."

" What do you mean?"

You know, one after the other . . . My God, have I got my wallet, my bag, my pen, my glasses, my rail ticket etc."

"No, I suppose that it's this case I have been trying for the last week. Now is decision and judgement time and I just can't make up my mind. It has been worrying me for days."

This seemed to account for the haggard look.

"Have you considered what I gather is called 'the greater shit principal'?"

"Oh yes, both parties are such utter shits that it is not possible to prefer one to the other on that basis?"

"If they are both that bad, why worry? One or the other; what the hell."

"I suppose it's the weakness of indecision."

"Anyway, what will you do if you really can't decide and have to stop agonising?"

"Spin a coin I imagine."

"You can't mean that?"

"Oh yes. Much weightier matters, matters of national importance are so decided. After all the toss of a coin decides who will bat on the first day's wicket in a test match?"

Was he joking?

94. Pretty Woman

Circa 1970, somewhere in Buckinghamshire, lived a lady, who had an account at the nearby Natwest Bank. She lived alone in a little old Georgian house with sash windows and was a bit of a recluse. Few knew her and even they learned very little about her. She was slim and managed to look very elegant in what were smart but old and out of fashion clothes.

She had had her account at the Natwest Bank for several years. One day in the autumn she said that she had mislaid a far from finished cheque book. The bank was quick to oblige her with another: its staff, male and female, were greatly taken with her for not only was she elegant but she was gracious in manner and lovely to look at, with her fine features, long black hair, tastefully streaked with her own genuine grey (she made no attempt to deny age) and the largest of soft grey eyes. The one thing she did not have was money.

With her bank account came a cheque card. Suddenly a number of her cheques were presented to the bank for payment. Each one was written for a substantial sum close to that which, with use of her card, the bank was bound to honour: only one was needed to wipe out the paltry balance in her account.

Sure that this must reflect some aberration, the bank manager telephoned her, several times but always he got no reply. So he wrote her a letter asking her please to come and see him as a matter of urgency as soon as possible. He got no response. The following day a veritable sheaf of her cheques was presented for payment, by the bank.

Becoming concerned he decided to go and see her and ask her please to hand over her cheque card. At her house he knocked on the front door, several times. Nobody answered. Then she appeared at an upstairs window. She smiled, charming as ever, and waved to him: but she did not come to the door.

He had no alternative but to return to the bank and alert the police. Back in his office he was informed that all her remaining cheques had been presented for payment each of sums close to the maximum covered by her card. No tradesman was to suffer, only the bank.

It was not long before she found herself in Holloway prison awaiting trial for various crimes of dishonesty. Why she was detained history does not relate, for she was without previous conviction.

A barrister, instructed on legal aid to defend her, came to visit.

He sat down opposite her at a small wooden table as the heavy cell door clanged behind and the warder left. The solicitor introduced them before he produced a written statement which, going straight to business, he invited her to read

"It is the testimony of your bank manager," he said.

After a little he asked:

"Is there anything you wish to dispute?"

"No."

"Did you get his letter?"

"Yes."

"Why did you not respond?"

"Because I needed my banker's card still."

"Did he come to your house?"

"Yes."

"Did you wave to him from an upstairs window but decline to let him in or to speak with him?"

"Yes."

The young man was overcome. He had watched her as she spoke. Despite her predicament she was immaculately groomed and lovely as ever. He shook his head miserably.

"You will have to plead guilty."

"Of course."

"Why, why?" He asked. "Help me. What am I to say to the judge on your behalf?"

She turned and for a few moments, through the bars in the lattice of her cell, looked out across the grey bleak prison yard. She turned to face him. He felt a strange magnetism from her doleful grey eyes. Her voice was soft and low.

"I have not had an easy or a happy life. I'd rather not tell you about it. There came a time when I thought I would like perhaps to have some of the things I have never had and should like to have had. You see, the bank could so easily afford them."

95. Technology

Gone are the days when barristers laboriously wrote out in manuscript their opinions and pleadings before handing them to a
typist, usually employed by their chambers. The advent of the
word processor has seen to all that. Now barristers type their own
written work, correct any errors and print out the finished product
ready for despatch to the awaiting solicitor. The time saved is
incalculable.

In the days gone by, after the initial lengthy hand writing process,
the typed version might come back from the typist with a greater or
lesser number of errors. If the number was small, the document
could be corrected in ink and a rather messy product sent out. If
the number was too great, a complete re-type would be called for
giving rise to further delay and the need again to re-check.

It was in Chancery chambers that typing often caused gnashing of
teeth, brought forth blasphemy and oaths on the grand scale. Their
documents frequently made reference to The Public Trustee. Re-
types, delay and expense were too often caused by a recurring error,
which the typists seemed quite incapable of avoiding and which
made a re-type absolutely essential: omission of the L in Public
Trustee.

96. Wrong time

A barrister, whose substantial junior practice was almost entirely
civil, found his name on an 'Attorney's list'. How this came about
he never knew: it meant that he received regular instructions to
prosecute in murder cases. These were not fashionable matters
calculated to catch the headlines. Rather they were domestic,

tragic and low key, reflecting the sadness in society. One tramp, high on meths, would kill another in a dispute over siting of a cardboard box residence under Waterloo Bridge in London.

At trial he always had Queen's Counsel to conduct the case. His job had been to advise on the evidence and in particular what material to divulge to the defence: the latter he found easy, usually everything.

One case stood out in his memory as reflecting human tragedy and awfulness in full measure. On opening (removing the white tape: tape of such a colour traditionally accompanies instructions from a State Department, which does not use the usual red) the papers he went first to the photographs. On the mortuary's slab lay the body of a very beautiful young woman. A waxen stillness of death showed in a lovely face. A superimposed arrow pointed to what looked like a small cut on her thigh, midway above the right knee below the hip.

Reading into the statements he learned that she had been a model of perfection and her father's pride and joy: sensible, loving, clever and lovely to look at. Herein lay a prime example of life's inherent unfairness. She had a younger sister, who was far from good looking, who was rebellious and who had got into bad company.

One evening, when the two were alone in the house, there was a row in the kitchen. The younger girl would not listen to the good sense directed by big sister and, losing her temper, on impulse took a kitchen knife and thrust it at that sister. By the sheerest of bad luck it struck the femoral artery: her sister died in moments surrounded by a massive pool of blood. Stricken with horror at what she had done, in panic she fled the house, before stopping to phone for an ambulance.

Their father, a mild man nearing retirement, returning home from a council meeting, was of course oblivious of the horrific scenario about to confront him and destroy the rest of his life: his lovely favourite daughter, lifeless on the kitchen floor in a lake of blood. On arrival he found two ambulance men trying to open his front door. He walked up to them and diffidently inquired:

"Can I help you?"

"Just leave us alone mate."

But he persisted.

"Please tell me what's going on?"

"Look, why don't you just fuck off?"

Not the time.

97. The Rule of Law

"The Rule of Law." After analysis by Professor A. V. Dicey in his famous work of 1885, *Introduction to the Study of the Law of the Constitution* where it was shown to be basic to the UK Constitution, the expression came into general, if too often indiscriminate, usage. It embraced a number of related concepts, including: the supremacy of the ordinary or regular law free of arbitrary or prerogative influence: no man is above the law: that there should be access to the law so as to enable the citizen to determine the consequences of his conduct. Judges should give reasoned judgements in open court and should follow precedent. Laws should not be retrospective. Certain Latin maxims reflect the The Rule of Law: *nullum crimen sine lege, nulla poena sine lege* (no crime . . . no punishment without a law . . . identifiable and in force). For an authoritative and full update see Tom Bingham's (Baron Bingham of Cornhill's) '*The Rule of Law*' published 2010.

Fresh from student learning of the law, and with a vague grasp still of the meaning of The Rule of Law, a young barrister went to Madrid at Easter circa 1964. Spain was ruled then by General Francisco Franco. The young man went as much to see a young Spanish woman, who he had met working for the Spanish Embassy in London, as to see the capital city. She was not working and in a few short days they visited so much, including the Retiro and the Prado. For their visit to the Prado, she borrowed her father's Seat motor car and parked it nearby in a time restricted area. Inside they moved from one masterpiece to another until presently he cautioned:

"Getting short of time with the car."

He was mindful of the fact that, as an English gentleman and the 'without which not' of the car's use, he would feel obliged to pay any penalty incurred.

"Don worry" she replied apparently unmoved.

When time was nearly up, he became agitated and concerned. Her reaction to reminder remained exactly the same. Then they were distracted by Velazquezs, El Grecos and Goya's nude and well clad Maja. But ultimately, absorbed by the 3rd May 1808, those anguished faces of stout patriots and Napoleon's dark and faceless firing squad, he forgot for a few moments. Then the emergency shot suddenly back into his mind. They had now badly overshot their time limit.

"My God the car" he said.

She looked at him with a calm and sad despairing resignation.

"Look Englishman, you have to be worry so much about this car parking. You don' worry. If we will be finding on the car a ticket, I give it to my father, he give it to the minister *de justitia* and nothing happen."

He was taken aback. 'Rule of law?!'

98. Murder Case

John Trenton, arrived home at nearly nine o'clock. A commuting barrister he was tired. His wife, Rosalind, opened the front door.

"Sorry to be late, he said "there's been a shooting on the train."

"Goodness! Tell me later. Peter, your clerk has been on. David Smith has gone part heard and you have to take on one of his other cases tomorrow. . . ."

"How can I do that? Look at the time, and I have no papers."

"As a shooting evidently meant that he couldn't get hold of you, he's taken the liberty of sending them by courier."

She pointed to a parcel of A4 papers a foot high on the hall table. Trenton blasphemed.

"I can't read that lot, never mind be ready for trial in the morning. For God's sake."

Realistic resignation quickly took over.

"Better try: get on with it . . . . all night effort. Peter's going to die for this."

The robust Rosalind was unusually sympathetic.

"You'll be alright. You've managed such crises before."

She brought black coffee and dinner to his study as he wrestled with oceans of paper and adrenalin production reached near tsunami proportions. The issues were numerous and complicated. Insofar as he understood the case, it seemed a loser.

He retired to bed at 4 o'clock exhausted and depressed and, surprisingly, slept for a little.

However well prepared, most barristers seldom feel quite ready for trial and, despite a deceptive air of assurance, arrive at court weak with nervous tension having slept very little: so much worse when they really are seriously unready.

Trenton arrived outside court six in the Royal Courts of Justice, robed and in a lather of apprehension. Quite a crowd had gathered. He needed to confer urgently with his solicitor, whom he didn't know and called out the name of his case, Jones v Wells. No response. A very tall barrister however pricked up his ears and ambled languidly over.

"I'm Bowles, Patrick Bowles, your opponent for the Plaintiff (claimant) in Jones v Wells. David Smith I presume?"

"Well, no. Trenton, John Trenton."

"Oh dear. Smith sick?"

"Otherwise detained."

"That's as well. Ashamed of his pleadings?"

Trenton rather agreed but took exception and didn't respond.

"*Qui non negat confitetur*" (he who does not deny admits) said Bowles, grinning the self satisfaction of what he saw as preliminary one-upmanship in use of an unusual Latin version.

"You'll get a rough ride from Olet. He's hot on pleadings."

Bowles had embarked upon the usual pre-trial intimidatory 'banter'. His approach was more ruthlessly straightforward than usual. As the pleader, he had been: in the case from the outset. His advantage was immense.

"You can't have been in this devilishly complex case for very long."

"Long enough."

"I wonder. You see I rang last night to speak with Smith. By six fifty precisely he was not back and was ostensibly still in this case. Perhaps we should have a little chat."

They wandered in silence along the stone corridor until they reached on their left one of those eddy-like areas off the main passageway, into which Bowles guided Trenton, who, manoeuvered skilfully, ended up with his back to a corner and Bowles standing face to face, towering over him, his legs a little astride. His right hand held his brief (much thinner than that of Trenton), his left was hidden under his gown, apparently inserted in the right hand inside pen/wallet pocket of his jacket: as Napoleon is often pictured.

"Don't think that I am deceived by those yellow flag stickers sprouting from your brief. Do you pretend that each represents a document, which you consider important? Have you even read them?"

He asked several further penetrating questions, which Trenton evaded or declined to answer, hoping to conceal his humiliating ignorance: but each time Bowles leered gloating satisfaction at his patent discomfort.

"You've had so little time, poor fellow."

Stung, Trenton replied. "I'm not here for discussion. Tell me what figure you ask for damages. I'll convey it to my clients. If you can't or won't do that I can't help you".

If they are here yet, he thought as, leering continuously Bowles edged closer, like one with halitosis, until eye-ball to eye-ball, he was only inches away.

"Oh, I'm going to ask for an awful lot of money. Your insurance man will never wear it. You are going to have to fight this case and it's going to be so terribly embarrassing because this judge is a stickler and you haven't read half the papers, have you?"

"What figure do you ask . . . . ?"

" . . . have you? Have you?" he went on louder and louder, ignoring Trenton's question.

Then a triumphant cackle before his voice dropped to a whisper.

"But my dear boy do not distress yourself . . . ."

He drew his left hand suddenly from his inside breast pocket.

" . . . because you see I'm going to kill you!"

It held a small pistol. He fired, point blank. 'Lord, Lord hethought, what pain it was to die' as Trenton sat bolt upright in bed.

"What is the matter?" groaned a bleary Rosalind.

"Just that Barrister's recurring nightmare, that I've arrived at court hopelessly under-prepared."

"But you've had plenty of those, why so violent?"

"Just more vivid, nastier and rather final this time! What time is it?"

99. *Reality*

Relief was short lived. John Trenton had now to face the real thing. He takes up: "I got straight up and breakfasted on tea and a slice of toast with Rosalind. She was less robust than usual, anxious perhaps that her man shouldn't crack. I felt sick inside with apprehension and fatigue though the adrenalin began again to flow and I managed to read a bit more on the train.

It seemed no time before I stood, robed but unready, outside court seven: listed before Stevens J. Could be worse, I thought. The awful dream seemed to be with me still as I imagined pain in my chest.

My solicitor appeared, identified himself and thanked me for taking on the case at such short notice. The insurance claims manager with him did likewise. Their gratitude embarrassed me for I feared that awful disaster may yet follow.

We agreed to abandon the issue of liability. How much to pay remained.

The insurance man was a civil fellow.

"At what do you value the claim?" he asked.

"Approx £270,000" I said.

"Much the same as myself. If you can get me out of this for £250,000 or under I shall be more than happy. I shall of course have to pay their costs: there is no money in court."

My opponent arrived late. They had got in Queen's Counsel. James Reid QC (a fictitious name). I knew of him and his considerable reputation. He beckoned me over. Business-like and unfriendly he was brisk and to the point.

"You concede liability of course? Your position is hopeless."

"No. You are put to formal proof."

"You can't mean it? I shall ask for indemnity costs."

"Those are my instructions."

I bluffed of course but thought that I detected discomfort.

"Very well, if we are to achieve anything we must look at quantum. We will accept £230,000 together with costs and not a penny less. I do not intend to mess about with calculations. This is not a usual approach but I make it clear that there is no room for negotiation."

I jumped inwardly for joy. I was already off the hook. But I shook my head solemnly.

"I doubt that my very experienced claims manager will entertain anything like such a sum but I will of course put it to him for what it is worth."

My insurance man was ecstatic and seemed to think that this was something to do with me. Hiding our jubilation we maintained glum faces as we agreed to offer £220,000.

Reid declared disinterest. Said he would advise rejection and returned again to ask the full £230,000.

"Look." I said to Reid "if you can persuade your client to come down just a little, then we may be in business. My insurer may up his offer just the tiniest bit to dispose of the matter."

"I shall inform him but advise against."

He came back almost immediately.

"We will accept £225,000 and costs of course."

"You may have £222,500 with costs."

"Done."

I never knew his problem. He had a very young junior not on the pleadings and perhaps, like myself, had come very late into the case. Or perhaps his client did not want to give evidence or they had missed a head of damage or were just not in a position to effect proof. Or might the learned QC have had a very lucrative case lined up for the Monday following, which he would have had to pass to another if our case had been contested?

Our ecstatic claims manager treated us to lunch at El Vino and we drank *Chateau Lafite 1975, 1er Cru Pauillac*!

100. Wrongful Arrest

Very late one night two on duty police officers in a police patrol car came across a new and shiny Rolls Royce car travelling west along the M4 motorway. They drove for some distance far behind it, then noticed that it had pulled onto the hard shoulder and that a man was relieving himself down an adjoining bank. They drew up behind and approached the man, dinner jacketed, now evidently greatly relieved but incoherently drunk. Beyond "Greetings off-ishers" conversation was virtually impossible. Decision was taken to drive him to the police station. The key to the Rolls Royce was in the ignition: the car was locked and could be collected next day. He couldn't be left in charge and was bundled unceremoniously into the police car. They set out. After a little the police driver observed uncomfortably to his colleague:

"The Rolls Royce is following behind: the driver has a peaked cap! Gawd! Do you think what I think?"

101. Good judge

One Friday afternoon a High court judge returned to court after an agreeable lunch with benchers in his Inn of Court. It was a hot and humid summers day in late July, approaching the long vacation. His Lordship was sprightly for a man approaching retirement and looked forward to having the time to do so much. He had not become grumpy, had not developed judgeitis and suffered fools (not silly fools) if not gladly. with a gentle tolerance.

On this particular day he was anxious to adjourn not later than four o'clock. A dinner appointment meant catching a train home, collecting his wife, having a bath, changing and driving some forty miles. That seemed to be a comfortable prospect as he put on his judicial robes and reflected on the matter before him in which there remained no more than a tidying up exercise likely to take about an hour. A knock on the door was his clerk.

"An application been slipped in, estimated at one hour Sir."

Blast, he thought. That could make his time schedule tight and stressful.

"Just one other thing I'm asked to tell you Sir, it's *ex parte* (only one party appearing) and the first case of a young lady counsel, who is very nervous; she hasn't had long for preparation."

Blast again, he thought, as his social plans seemed likely to disintegrate into potential disaster.

His unfinished morning case he managed to hurry along and it finished within the hour. The young woman counsel's case followed. What she asked seemed relatively straightforward. She looked very young and was very pretty. But appealing looks were not to help her as initial judicial optimism began to crumble while she stumbled through what was for her unfamiliar territory. Further she was quite unable to cope with some arithmetic, which it involved. As time slipped away and with his eye on the four thirty train, he became somewhat tetchy.

"May I suggest another, and if I may say so speedier, way of going about this . . . please, I have read ahead, the rest of this aspect has no relevance to this application and need not be dealt with . . . need we repeat the introductory material, which seems to be duplicated . . ."

His Lordship's tone of voice became progressively less than friendly as it passed three thirty five. Suddenly he erupted.

"I shall adjourn for ten minutes."

He gathered up his papers and departed only to return after nine minutes.

"I think that this is the order you ask." He said, addressing counsel and handing down to her two sheets of paper.

"And I have done for you the supporting mathematics, which you may like to check."

He hoped that she wouldn't and she didn't. The court adjourned at five to four and His Lordship bustled somewhat ungraciously out of court, able, only just and not without anxiety, to get home in time. It had been near thing.

On the train journey home he thought back over the afternoon and embarrassed himself. What a bastard I was, he thought.

On the Monday morning following he travelled to London on the train with a colleague and told him of how he had behaved on the Friday afternoon last.

"Do you think, he asked at last, that I was a real bastard?"

"Probably, but as you are clearly concerned, I think that you are still probably a pretty good judge."

Beware of judges on Fridays p.m., when even nice judges can be disagreeable.

102. With a leader

A middle aged junior barrister was very surprised when a murder case landed on his desk. He was a London practitioner and neither a circuiteer nor a criminal lawyer, though he did have some recent experience of crime at a lower level when sitting as a recorder. Colour police photographs of the horribly mutilated deceased victim, lying very dead on the mortuary slab, made him queasy. He moved quickly on and was glad to note that he would have with him a leader, a QC, to conduct most of, and the important parts of, the case at trial.

Trial was to be at Assize up north and he was so grateful when his leader, who lived up there, invited him to stay for the duration of the hearing. The evening before trial he took a train and met his leader at his chambers and was driven to his home.

Dinner with him and his charming and eminently presentable wife was very congenial. The QC was evidently on top of the case and felt no need to talk shop. Conversation ranged over many topics. She had a particular interest in the Romans in Britain and in particular Clodius Albinus, governor of the Province of Britannia, whose legions in AD 193 declared him emperor of Rome (but he didn't last long!) and Carausius, who was commander of the Roman North Sea Fleet until in 286 he declared himself independent of Rome and Emperor of Britannia.

Next day was to be a heavy day and all retired early to bed. Our barrister re-read his brief and made some notes. Hard to get a case up in detail when somebody else was going to conduct all or most of it. But leaders had a habit of saying spontaneously "take the next witness, would you please?" Worse still they might be ill or even die, leaving their junior to take over: not likely but engendering a very real contingent discomfort. Part of the justification of the two counsel rule is that such an event should not mean that the trial be abandoned with all that consequent inconvenience, expense and waste of time.

He got into bed at last. His eyes wandered wearily over books in a small bookcase beside the bed. Some Dickens. A Tale of Two Cities, Wordsworth Poems, John Buchan, an Oxford Dictionary. Fast closing eyes opened suddenly wider as they fixed upon a prominent red hardback: 'Sex for the Single Visiting Guest'. He declined to pull it out as he wondered. Could it be soft, even hard porn? Or might it be erotic arousing short stories? There appeared to be no author and he did not recognise the publisher. Intriguing. Curiosity got the better of his fatigue at last. He pulled it from the shelf. He opened it up. Blank page followed blank page . . . all were blank, save the very last one . . . and he nearly missed it. 'Bad luck' it said.

103. Stopped by Police

To be the bearer of an historic and famous name is not always advantageous. When an undergraduate at Oxford, circa 1959, the young Winston Churchill (grandson of Sir Winston and son of Randolph) was stopped for speeding in the Witney Road. Asked by the police officer for his name, he replied "Winston Churchill" and was met with an unamused, hostile response.

"If you continue to be funny with me I'll book you for wasting police time, obstructing the course of justice . . ."

104. Life saver

A young barrister drove to his parent's home very late one Friday night (Saturday morning ?). En route he became aware of a police car pulling out of a side road behind. It began to follow him. He was pleased that (unusually for a Friday night) he had not had as much as even half a pint of beer to drink and drove immaculately, signalling for every parked car he passed and maintaining a speed of twenty eight m.p.h. After a little he thought he would like to shake off the police pursuit, so he turned right into a side road intending to return to the main road. The police car followed. After return to the main road, a little unnerved for no good reason he could think of, he decided to repeat the exercise a little further on. The police car followed again but this time flashed its lights, overtook him and stopped.

Out spilled two police officers. They approached his car with a slow nonchalent swagger, looking distinctly unfriendly, not to say menacing. He wound down his window.

"Can I help you officer?" he said, not entirely without some mild apprehension. They stood silent for a few moments. Then one spoke.

"We are of the opinion that you have been being funny with us."

"If by funny you mean driving immaculately since you joined me behind, so that I have given you no reason for stopping me, I agree."

The officers were not amused. They really meant what they said, 'being funny' with them but they did not enlighten him as to how or why. Then he had a horrid thought. Were they going to fix him to bolster their crime statistics? He was suddenly most uncomfortable.

"This is clearly no joking matter," he said, getting out of his car.

"You had better tell me what you say constitutes 'being funny' with you."

"We think you know."

"I have no faint idea. You must tell me. And, please your note-books. We will all write down what we each say happened and we will all sign."

"OK Mr Clever . . . every time you passed a stationary car and each time you turned right into side roads, you gave us a left hand indication. Did you think that was funny?"

"I don't think I did, and no, it would not be funny."

"Do you say that we imagined it or made it up? That could be very serious."

"No, but I do not to my knowledge suffer from a neurological condition which affects adversely what I think I intend. Let us test both myself and the machinery."

He started the engine and asked the officers to witness that he moved the signal control lever to the turning right position. They then moved to the rear of the car. The left hand indicator light was flashing. Suddenly there were two smiling friendly policemen.

"How come?" asked one.

"I would guess that in effecting recently some frontal repairs someone has misplaced an electric lead."

The officers wished him a safe journey home and invited him to take care.

"Reckon we probably saved your life," said one.

105. Personal Injury

The personal injury (PI) case takes up much of the time of judges in the Queen's Bench Division of the High Court. In particular assessment of the appropriate sum of money to be awarded as damages for injuries sustained, be it in a motor accident, an industrial accident or sometimes plain falling over a raised paving stone. The main head of damage (especially in less serious cases) is known as 'general damages for pain, suffering and loss of amenity' and is awarded as a lump sum.

Back injuries regularly provide scope for argument. Doctors are not able to speak confidently as to the extent and/or intensity of pain and disability attributable to them. Often no organic cause can be found and medical opinion can vary greatly. Allegations of exaggeration or malingering may accordingly have to be decided by a judge. The man who complains of intense pain enabling him to do practically nothing may be surprised to learn that inquiry agents, instructed by insurers, have filmed him digging his vegetable garden for long periods of time. Shoulder injuries are another area where doctors are not always able to make or agree confident assessments and predictions.

A visitor to the public gallery may be lucky enough to witness something like the revelatory forensic exercise following:

Counsel for the Defendant to the claimant (plaintiff) in the witness box: "You have shown this court just how high you can raise your arm. Please show us again."

Claimant raises right arm to just below the level of the injured shoulder.

Counsel: "Could you not raise it just a little higher?"

Claimant: "No."

Counsel: "Please try."

Claimant winces and groans but manages about an inch higher.

Counsel: "So because of this you are unable to lift clothes into hanging cupboards, to chop logs, to pick apples and plums from your various trees: is that right?"

Claimant: "Yes."

Counsel: "Above all you cannot reach up for the books you need at your work?"

Claimant: "That's right."

Counsel: "You are a man of 40 now and played a lot of tennis, not now possible?"

Claimant: "Right."

Counsel: "You were quite good at it?"

Claimant: "Well I won my club championship once . . ."

All this seemed to be counter-productive, emphasising the disabilities complained of. The exchange of question and answer however becomes enthusiastic and gathers momentum. The claimant is animated as it ranges for a little over Pete Sampras, Roger Federer, Rafael Nadal (Raffa) and Andy Murray before returning to the claimant himself. There is danger that the judge might intervene to terminate this line of time wasting questioning unless its relevance can be explained.

Counsel: "Am I right in thinking that on the occasion of your winning the club competition you won your two final service games by serving eight aces?"

Counsel seldom asks such a question unless he knows the answer. "Yes" . . . he smiles pride at the memory.

Counsel: "And at that time how high could you raise your arm?"

His arm shoots spontaneously up and over his head!

QED.

143

106. Fax machine

As one of Her Majesty's Judges of the Queen's Bench Division donned his robes one Monday morning, he remarked to his clerk that the judgment he had reserved on the Thursday before, which he was about to deliver, had run to 8,000 words and taken up most of his weekend.

"Just look it out please, it's at the top in my briefcase. I have half an hour and could perhaps rephrase one or two passages."

"I don't find it," said his clerk presently.

"Oh come," said His Lordship, robed now and striding across the room where he personally rummaged through his briefcase.

"My God!" Less than judicial expletives followed.

"You're right I've left it at home."

"Does Your Lordship not have one of those new fax machines?"

"Indeed I have . . . ."

"Then her Ladyship could perhaps fax it here?"

"She could but she's not at home: incommunicado on some ramble."

"Oh dear! That's really faxed things up."

107. Franglais

Circa 1991 a senior junior barrister received instructions to give an opinion on English Law to be used to establish a point central to proceedings in a French Appeal Court. He was a little diffident. The matter was difficult. He spoke to Anthony his solicitor.

"Don't you think that this is a case for a leader's (QC's) opinion? Very complicated and an awful lot of money involved. Disastrous cost if my view were to be wrong. More important you could be criticised for instructing junior counsel."

"I would like you to write the opinion. If you can't put QC after your name, how about 'BA Hons Oxon'?"

"That is something I have never done."

"I'm instructing you to do it now."

The opinion went to France with the words 'BA Hons Oxon' appearing beneath the signature of the writer. The French judges accepted it *in toto*. That they were not influenced in the slightest by the qualification or status of the signatory was plain. They identified him as l'Avocat à Londres but in the course of argument at trial referred regularly to the opinion of Monsieur Bahons-Oxon!!

108. Big Chance

The El Vino wine bar at 47, Fleet Street has featured already (Tales 68 and 99). Over the years its fine wines provided therapeutic oblivion to all who entered: in particular to journalists and lawyers and later, when the press left Fleet Street, mainly to lawyers. In its confines the stresses of the day's conflict would fade gently away as wine flowed agreeably into their veins. Dickensian characters might be seen there and learning might be acquired: that Madame de Pompadour had declared champagne to be the only wine that a woman could drink and continue afterwards to look beautiful and that Napoleon's opinion, that 'in victory you deserve it, in defeat you need it', justified the evening habit of too many barristers whatever the outcome of their day in court. El Vino itself tendered good promotional advice 'you cannot drink too much of it, you can only drink it too quickly'.

For known customers the 'El Vino Bank' would readily cash cheques and wine tastings were held by invitation. On these occasions little use was made of the spittoon, even though just a few of the finest, and unthinkably expensive, wines were proffered: the big chance for most to experience a little of how the other half lived: a chance to savour the equivalent in 2010 of Chateau Mouton Rothschild 1er Cru Pauillac, a chance too often denied to any but the earliest on the scene. On one occasion a marginally latecomer, hoping for a taste of nectar, managed eventually to find this prize, on an isolated small table hidden by a surround of pleased and happy looking tasters. But alas all three bottles were virtually drained of content. Upbraided, one villain responded with a grin "I'm so sorry. It's my friend here. He can't make up his mind."

109. VIPs

Circa 1962. Young men in chambers offered a pupil a lift for part of his journey home. He accepted, pleased and grateful, and, in company with three others, made his way to their car, which was parked in King's Bench Walk. They all climbed in. The pupil sat in the back seat with a Scot, who was in jovial mood.

As they drove out of the Temple and into Tudor Street, they came to an abrupt halt on account apparently of some incident at the junction with Bouverie Street. Almost on the instant a man appeared and looked into their car: a newspaper reporter probably from the nearby Evening Standard offices. "Anybody important in here?" he asked excitedly. The driver shook his head as did his front seat passenger. The pupil was suitably silent and the disappointed reporter made to depart when a distinctly Scottish voice from the back of the car rewarded him. "I'm in here and I'm bloody important."

The phenomenon of time and place. Look today into a well preserved Roman arena and see an impressive scene of tranquillity. Hard to imagine the appalling scenes of gladiatorial contest to the death and other savage entertainment, some two thousand years ago. On another level, were the same reporter to look inside that car in 2009, forty seven years on, and ask the same question of three of the same occupants, he could have heard the front passenger say "I am a retired Lord Justice of Appeal." The driver could have said (modesty probably not permitting) "I have been a Lord of Appeal in Ordinary, Lord Chief Justice of England and Wales, Master of the Rolls and Senior Law Lord". No longer of this world, the Scot alas would not have been there to entertain and tell that he had been a Law Commissioner. The pupil merely relates a thought and a memory.

AUTHOR'S NOTE

I finish by recording two episodes involving giants of the justice system; episodes which, respectively, I was lucky and privileged enough to have seen and be involved in and which have left abiding and happy memory. And a third contrasting historical episode, which reminds us of how lucky we have been and in which, happily, I was not and could not have been involved.

110. Colossus

Lord Denning of Whitchurch. A man who had academics hopping up and down when I was an undergraduate in 1960. Had his decision in that famous case, Central London Property Trust Ltd. v High Trees House Ltd.,([1947] K.B 130) taken his very personal brand of merit related flexibility beyond the permissible bounds of existing law?

He advanced from a judge of Queen's Bench Division (appointed 1944), through the Court of appeal (as Lord Justice) up to the House of Lords and then back to the Court of Appeal, as Master of the Rolls, where he could have a much greater influence on the direction of the law's development, since so much appellate litigation did not advance beyond that court. He retired in 1982 after 38 years on the bench.

I appeared in his court only twice, and when he was Master of the Rolls. Each time the merits swept all else aside. It is however not my own cases but what I witnessed while waiting to come on in the court that I remember most happily and record.

He presided over a three-judge court of appeal, flanked by two Lords Justices. A litigant in person stood at the front and addressed them. I do not remember what about. I sat behind and watched.

My interest was in a man, who was already a legend, not in the litigant's problems. The litigant seemed to have been speaking for some time. Lord Denning listened intently. Then suddenly he intervened, gently:

"Mr Smith I am very sorry to interrupt you, but you see you have told us all about your problems twice and are embarking on the third time. You may take it that we understand. We don't think that it will help you if you tell us all over again . . ."

The gentle Hampshire burr in his voice added a special dimension to the civility with which he treated this man.

" . . . . now you just sit down please."

Be a good boy! He smiled as he wagged a long finger like a benign but firm schoolmaster before (after consulting his two fellow judges) reading a short *ex tempore* judgement and, in the kindliest way, gently dismissing Mr Smith's appeal and thanking him for his courtesy and helpful assistance.

He clearly knew the substance of 2 Corinthians 11.19: 'For ye suffer fools gladly, seeing ye yourselves are wise.' He was a model of patience, charm and firm courtesy. No advocate, however mean or inadequate was allowed to feel obtuse, wanting or uncomfortable in his court.

111. Role Model

Circa 1968 I was a junior junior (sic) barrister. I received instructions to advise in a matter of part performance, an equitable remedy relating to contracts affecting interests in land where there was no note or memorandum in writing as was required by S. 40(1) of the Law of Property Act 1925. This could be an area of law subtle and difficult: too esoteric for further detailed explanation here. The case before me seemed notwithstanding to be quite a

149

straightforward one. I advised confidently in writing and never expected to see the matter again: the opposing party would surely cave in. But no. Proceedings had to be commenced in the Chancery Division of the High Court and it fell to me to draft the statement of claim. Defence followed: I couldn't see that there was any defence. Yet the pleader was no slouch: a man who knew his stuff. I began to doubt myself.

The Chancery Division was a fearsome place for common lawyers; all those hidden restrictive practices likely to surface and explode like torpedoes: designed, it was said, by the Chancery boys to embarrass and frighten off the common lawyers. I was unnerved but liked to feel sure that this was bravado on the part of the Defendant and that at a later stage he would seek settlement. But no.

The case entered the list. I checked everything. The law was possibly not as straightforward as I had thought, but it was clear enough and we had proof. Little is so unnerving for a barrister as a case he can't see how he can lose. Why do they contest it? I asked myself. Have I missed or misunderstood something? I advised on evidence: a couple of similar sketch plans were needed. The list came out the night before trial in the dread, unfamiliar, booby-trapped Chancery Division.

My judge was to be none other than the Vice-Chancellor, Pennycuick J., the senior Chancery judge and head of that division; a man of whom I had no knowledge or experience. I slept little that night. Next day I made my way to court in a positive lather of apprehension. It is not easy for those who are not advocates to understand the nervous pre-trial tension that can build up. My opponent appeared. He introduced himself (a chancery practitioner) but made no approach to compromise. A fight was on.

The court assembled. His Lordship entered, bowed and sat down.

"Yes Mr Gray" he said after re-arranging some papers in front of him. Through the usher my solicitor handed him up one of the agreed sketch plans. He sat silent while I opened, that is told him what the case was all about and outlined the applicable law to be considered. Then I called my first witness, a young man in his thirties.

My nervous anxiety did not improve as a state of utter confusion ensued.

The witness seemed quite unable to understand or coherently to answer my questions. At any moment I expected to have to batten down the hatches and weather a broadside of judicial irritation.

Suddenly I realised the possible problem and asked if I might see the sketch-plan in the witness box. It was the wrong one.

"My Lord, might I please see the sketch-plan which has been given to Your Lordship?"

"Certainly" he said handing it down: also the wrong one! This was the last straw and the culmination of all my fears.

"My Lord I must apologise profusely. Regrettably the witness and yourself have been looking at the wrong sketch-plan. I fear that Your Lordship may not have understood much, if any, of what I said in opening."

I braced myself ready to soak up a broadside of judicial grapeshot. Instead I was met with a broad reassuring smile.

"Mr Gray, I understood very little of what you told me but I wouldn't dream of interfering because at this stage you know so much more about it than I."

I think that in that moment that dear man saved my very life.

The case from then on was agreeably managed with his modest charm: a joy to experience and forever to remember. Here was another man familiar with 2 Corinthians 11.19.

All that I had feared had come to nothing: and I won that case in the end. Sir John Pennycuick. A name to be remembered. An example for all judges and indeed to all men.

112. Depravity

In 1685, after the protestant James Duke of Monmouth had failed to unseat the Catholic King James II, his supporters having been routed at the battle of Sedgemoor, a reign of terror prevailed in the West Country. Those who had thrown in their lot with the Duke were hunted down and subjected to a depraved brutality hard to believe. Lord Chief Justice Jeffreys presided over their trials, known as the Bloody Assizes held at Winchester, at which some two hundred and fifty death sentences were handed down. In his court witnesses and juries were bullied and put in fear. Those whose evidence did not go to guilt were intimidated and, where prosecution evidence was wanting, he was not above providing it himself in his summing up. Among the lists of those put to death, transported, flogged or fined was only one woman: Lady Alice Lisle, a widow in her seventies, who had allegedly fed and harboured one John Hicks, a wretch fleeing the vengeance of the victors. Details of her trial are recorded in Volume Eleven of Hansard's State Trials. Two quotes portray the atmosphere of this trial: the language used is perhaps indicative of the judge's fiendish relish in torment of all around. Judge to witness:

"I would not by an means in the world wish to frighten you with anything, or in any way tempt you to tell an untruth. I would however provoke you to tell the truth, and nothing but the truth. You have a precious immortal soul and there is nothing in the world equal to it in value." Evidence that might go to innocence attracted fierce remedial intervention.

"Mr Dunne have a care, for it may be that more of this is known than you think."

"My Lord I tell the truth."

"Well I only bid you have a care. Truth never wants subterfuge, it always likes to appear naked, it needs no enammeling nor any covering. But lying and canting and snivelling always appear in masquerade . . . you are a prevaricating, lying, snivelling rascal!"

Lady Alice was found guilty and sentenced to be burned alive, a sentence commuted by the King to beheading.

The End

BIBLIOGRAPHY

In writing this book I have consulted varied sources, more people than books. Here are as many books as I can remember using to a degree sufficient to warrant mention.

A Dictionary of Latin Words and Phrases. James Morwood. O.U.P. 1998 Advocates. David Pannick. Oxford Universty Press 1992.

Collins Pocket reference Thesaurus. 1999. Chief editor Patrick Hanks.

Compact Oxford English Dictionary 2nd edition 2003 revised. Edited Catherine Soanes. O.U.P.

Judges. David Pannick. Oxford University Press 1987.

New Pocket Dictionary of the Latin and English Languages. Eyre and Spottiswoode, London.

Osborn's Concise Law Dictionary, eighth edition, edited by Leslie Rutherford and Sheila Bone. Sweet and Maxwell.

Oxford dictionary of Law, fourth edition 1997 edited by Elizabeth A Martin. O.U.P.

Without My Wig. G.D. Roberts. QC Macmillan and co Ltd 1957.

INDEX

NOTE: A partial index intended mainly to enable the reader to trace some (not all) tales or entries when he or she cannot remember the heading but can recollect some of the content.

155

TABLE OF CASES